THE PSYCHODYNAMICS
OF HOSTILITY

THE PSYCHODYNAMICS OF HOSTILITY

Leon J. Saul, M.D.

Emeritus Professor of Psychiatry
Medical School of the University of Pennsylvania

Honorary Staff, Institute of the Pennsylvania Hospital

Emeritus Training Analyst
Philadelphia Psychoanalytic Institute

with

Barbara Wrubel

JASON ARONSON, INC.
NEW YORK

ISBN: 0-87668-241-7

Library of Congress Catalog Number: 75-37488

typeset by Frank Kotkov
         New York, N.Y.

Manufactured in the United States of America

to the children

PREFACE

The purpose of this book is to provide some basic psychiatric information about human hostility. It is also a call to the relevant sciences and to intelligent men and women everywhere to turn their attention to the world's most important and urgent danger: man's hostility to man. The fact that great strides are daily being made in the understanding of human nature and behavior rarely makes headlines. But it is true that the dream of man maturing fully and living peacefully with his fellow man is now as much within our reach *theoretically* as is the dream of space travel. What was unthinkable yesterday becomes tomorrow's reality.

What makes criminals and great men, what makes the loftiest achievements of the human spirit, and what makes the destruction, chaos, and unutterable bestiality and misery of war—this is now known. To apply such knowledge is a vast and enormously difficult task in human engineering, but it is only a practical task. To show that this is so and to focus attention upon it is the goal of this book.

It is a pleasure to thank Reid and Marion Baldridge, Dr. John R. Lion, Dr. John Spiegel, Dr. Thoburn Snyder, and Dr. Milton M. Miller for helping me obtain needed data, and especially Dr. Silas Warner, who has provided some of the clinical material. We would also like to acknowledge grateful appreciation to Susan Bender, a peerless secretary and assistant; June Strickland, librarian of the Institute of the Pennsylvania Hospital; and Clare Lynch O'Brien, who brought a keen editorial eye to the reading of the manuscript. And, of course, our gratitude to Rose Saul, for her patience and support, and to Peter Wrubel, for his unshakable faith and encouragement.

Certain of the chapters are based in part upon articles that appeared in technical journals, and for permission to publish these revised versions thanks are extended to *The Psychoanalytic Quarterly, The Proceedings of the American Philosophical Society,* and *The American Journal of Psychiatry.*

CONTENTS

THE PSYCHODYNAMICS
OF HOSTILITY

Part One

BIOLOGICAL ORIENTATION

On Seeing Weather-beaten Trees

"Is it as plainly shown
By slant and twist, which way
the wind hath blown?"

ADELAIDE CRAPSEY

Chapter 1

WHAT HOSTILITY IS

The threat to the survival of the human species by an astronomical accident is negligible. Man is now reasonably secure against the elements. Floods, earthquakes, volcanic eruptions, and tidal waves are by their very nature sporadic catastrophes and not general threats to mankind. Today, famine need no longer be a threat since we have the resources, technology, and manpower to produce ample food for the present population of the world, and we certainly have the wherewithal to control the population, which left unchecked would glut the earth.

Modern medicine has made such enormous strides that, although important problems remain, even the infectious diseases no longer are a major threat to humanity. Man is still endangered by cancer, heart disease, and the degenerative diseases, but breakthroughs in knowledge and control of these are likely to come soon.

The most dire threat to mankind today comes from man himself. The readiness of human beings to be hostile to each other is by far the greatest problem of mankind. It takes no marshalling of facts to establish this. Examples of hostility on a gross scale are everywhere to be found—tyrannical rule persists in many countries of the world; modern nations squander countless sums and resources on mobilization for global destruction; rates of violent crime, divorce, and child abuse ever increase to staggering dimensions. But the fact that man's brutality to man has bloodied every page of history and continues to do so does not mean that it is basic to human nature and as such inevitable. Certainly our observations of the behavior of other species would not offer support for such a thesis. With the nearly singular exception of man, sadistic cruelty and murder within a species is all but unknown in the rest of the animal kingdom. You would have to descend to the harvester ant to see anything even remotely like it. A close look at man's behavior reveals that it has all the earmarks, not of nature, but of sickness, of psychopathology.

To begin our investigation of man's hostility, let us formulate a working definition of the term. As a point of departure, we can say that hostility is the tendency of an organism to do something harmful to another organism or to itself. This is not just aggression, which is a term often used interchangeably with hostility. Some significant distinctions must be made between these terms. Following the dictionary we see that the word aggression has a Latin origin, *adgradi*, meaning to move toward or against. This movement need not be destructive; indeed, we can see how it would be desirable, for example, to be aggressive in the pursuit of constructive goals. Herein lies the telling contrast with the notion of hostility. Coming from the Latin word for enemy, *hostis*, hostility has none of the ambiguity implicit in aggression; it is always destructive, or at least aimed at destructive ends. Furthermore, unlike the word aggression, which is a term descriptive of behavior, hostility is a psychological term primarily denoting feeling and motivation. As such, it can properly be described dynamically; for example, as conscious or unconscious, as repressed, suppressed, or expressed, as active or passive. In contrast, to speak of repressed aggression strains the term, while the notion of passive aggression is a paradox if not a semantic and conceptual monstrosity.

As a technical definition we might hazard the following: Hostility is a motivating force—a conscious or unconscious impulse, tendency, intent, or reaction—aimed at injuring or destroying some object, animate or inanimate. In humans, hostility is usually accompanied by the feeling or emotion of anger.

Hostility can take almost limitless forms, can be used for every sort of purpose, and can range in intensity from a glance or a breath of gossip to vindictiveness, violence, brutality, and murder. Hostility is an essential evil in man. So fundamental is it and so constantly present as a central link in psychodynamics,* that symptoms can be arranged on a scale grading from the psychosomatic and conversion hysteria, in which the hostility is most inhibited and internal, through the classic neuroses with their anxieties, compulsions, and depressions, through the psychoses with extensive projection, to the acting-out range, wherein the hostility is turned masochistically against the self or criminally and even sadistically against others.

Hostility, if it causes psychosomatic, neurotic, or nonviolent psychotic symptoms or if it is expressed masochistically against the self, causes suffering to the individual and to those close to him but does not menace society. But when hostility takes the form of direct acting out, it breeds violence, crime, and senseless destruction of innocent victims, even children.

Man, as his written history clearly testifies, has always considered it important to understand the motives by which he lives, loves, and hates. But today, with the capacity for total destruction in his hands, man's ability to understand himself and to use that understanding for the prevention of violence is crucial to his very survival. Each individual is activated by strong asocial and antisocial motivations, as well as by social ones. Only by understanding these two sets of motives, the one against life and the one for it, can we maximize those that are prohuman and reduce those that are antihuman. All this seems clear enough, but there will be those who will resist understanding it nonetheless. Emotions are complex and difficult to understand at best, but discussions of hostility and its role in problems involving motivations of, for example, sex, dependency, and prestige arouse in most people such passionate feelings that true detachment in dealing with this subject is rare indeed.

Doubtless some of this stems from prejudice and rationalization. It seems that many people would like to believe, and in fact do believe, that hostility is inherited and therefore should be dismissed as something about which nothing, at least for the present, can be done. Others believe, falsely, that hostility is a strength, that without it men and women would be left defenseless in a world all too ready to attack and exploit the weak. Others, of course, resist the study of hostility just from the tendency of mankind to resist any new idea. The great physician William Harvey feared to make known what is now accepted as a commonplace fact—the circulation of the blood: "I not only fear injury to myself from the envy of a few, but I tremble lest I have mankind at large for my enemies, so much does wont and custom become second nature. Doctrine once sown strikes deeply at its root and respect for antiquity influences all men. Still the die is cast and my trust is in the love of truth and the candor of cultivated minds."

Besides such general reasons for shunning the problem of hostility, there are others more individual and deep-seated. Some people balk at accepting hostility as a psychological force because of hostile reactions within themselves. A friend of mine, hearing of this study, reacted quite unsympathetically. Because he was basically a man of good will, his reaction aroused my interest. He was one of those people whose hostilities were overinhibited when he was a child and as a result he has always felt that he lacks the capacity of self-defense even for proper purposes. In shunning this unpleasant conflict within himself, he reacted like an ostrich; he put his head in the sand and maintained that the less said about hostility the better.

The guilt that an individual feels for his own known hostile reactions and deeds may also impair objective understanding. The reason for this is that the feeling of guilt brings along with it conscience reactions and a need for punishment. Some people may even prefer punishment to cure and suffering to happiness. Indeed, in psychiatric practice it is not uncommon to see patients who truly feel that they do not deserve to be cured. This need for suffering, the masochism, is so widespread that it often extends to feelings about society in general, with a resulting attitude, usually unconscious, that mankind deserves its miseries and should not or cannot be helped toward a better life.

This resistance to facing and dealing with the central issue of man's hostility, whether consciously motivated or not, is nowhere more striking than in the writing of Freud. He began his study of the neuroses by focusing on the sexual drives. Although hostility is mentioned in the case histories, it was not until eight years before his death that Freud articulated any theoretical formulation of "unerotized aggression" (that is, hostility without sexual, sensual, or sensuous feelings). At this point so late in his life he was unable to give it the detailed clinical attention that he had earlier devoted to the libidinal impulses. However, Freud expanded his instinct theory into a broad dualistic view of life as fundamentally an interplay between the forces of creativity (Eros) and the forces of destruction and death (Thanatos). What is interesting to us here is not the specific content of Freud's theory, but rather the astonishment with which he acknowledges having overlooked the "tendency toward aggression," which he said constituted "the most powerful obstacle to culture." In *Civilization and Its Discontents* he wrote,

> I know that we have always had before our eyes manifestations of the destruction instinct fused with erotism, directed outwards and inwards in sadism and masochism, but I can no longer understand how we could have overlooked the universality of non-erotic aggression and destruction and could have omitted to give it its due significance in our interpretation of life . . . I can remember my own defensive attitude when the idea of an instinct of destruction first made its appearance in psychoanalytical literature and how long it took until I accepted it. That others should have shown the same resistance, and still show it, surprises me less. Those who love fairy tales do not like it when people speak of the innate tendencies of mankind toward aggression, destruction, and, in addition, cruelty.

But obviously the nature of this "innate tendency" can and should be studied—for the sake of our own survival. We can begin immediately by asking: Is hostility a drive or is it a reaction? Or, perhaps, is it both?

Chapter 2

HOSTILITY AND BIOLOGICAL ADAPTATION

If we observe an individual member of any species—a gold-fish, a mosquito, a python, or a man—we see two activities pre-dominating: the effort to survive and the effort to fulfill the life cycle. Whatever the vicissitudes of individual experience, the basic plan is always the same. First, there is development to ma-turity, then reproduction, with some care or provision for the young, then decline, and finally death. This cycle of life is not a remote scientific concept; it is a fundamental biological force that operates within all of us. Any attempt to deviate from it or any failure to fulfill it, brings difficulty and pain.

From a strictly global or astronomical point of view, man is, in essence, not very much. On this tiny planet within a tiny solar system, there has developed a combination of molecules in a jel-ly-like substance, about 85 percent water, which chemists call a colloidal suspension. One form of colloid we know as living matter or protoplasm. The earth's surface teems with this substance; man is only one form, though granted a highly complex one, of the biological life on this planet.

Why, some millions of years ago, did this human form of protoplasm take shape on the earth? Neither scientists, philosophers, nor men of religion have agreed upon a verifiable answer. But we do know how it has survived. This has been accomplished through its capacity to adapt to the conditions of life on this planet. The dinosaur, with its pea-sized brain and clumsy, lumbering body, did not survive; the ant, with its complex and sophisticated social organization, has existed far longer than man. But the fact that the human race exists today does not mean that it will automatically continue to survive. And most of us, for ourselves and our children, would not relish participation in its decay.

It is popularly believed that physical force, coupled with cunning and a dog-eat-dog attitude, is the best mechanism for guaranteeing the survival of the species. But scientific research offers no support for this supposition. As more and more work is done in this area, it becomes clear that each form of life uses at least two major mechanisms of adaptation: social cooperation and the fight-flight reflex.

According to the eminent biologist Warder C. Allee, a leading authority in this field, cooperation not only serves animals as a protection, but also as an aid to development. Allee's lifetime studies reveal that the organism living in association with others increases in size, swiftness, and the ability to recover from damage more quickly than those that are isolated. The latter prove much more susceptible to poisons and retardation and tend to suffer more often from hunger and the attacks of other animals.

It is Allee's conclusion that "no free living animal is solitary throughout his life history," and that the tendency of animals to aggregate is a primitive, unconscious drive. On its higher levels, these aggregations attain refinements of organization. We are all familiar with the advanced social life of bees and ants, with the way elephants gather in herds, wolves in packs, fish in schools, birds in flocks, and so on. The features of both leadership and class orders are found among animal organizations.

Just as there is the queen-worker-drone order among bees, there is the somewhat despotic peck order among hens and other species in confined societies. Each hen can peck those lower in the order than herself but must submit to pecks from those higher. Similarly, among lizards, there is a nip order. And the same type of domination-submission order is found in other species as well.

Social cooperation is also enhanced by various types of communication found throughout animal organizations. Mating calls, for example, exist in almost all forms of life. Bees dance in a certain way to inform their fellow hive-dwellers when and where honey can be found. Certain types of birds are signaled toward migration by leader-birds.

When we turn to human societies, we find greater complexity, but a similar tendency to group, to organize, and to communicate. Like other animals, it is only through social living and sharing that man has been able to protect himself and thus assure his continued survival. But there is one crucial difference that distinguishes human organization from animal groupings: only among human beings have organization and aggregation been used not only for protection from other animals, but also for attack on and destruction of their own kind. "One species of animal may destroy another," Allee writes in *Cooperation Among Animals*, "and individuals may kill other individuals, but *group* struggles to the death between members of the same species, such as occur in human warfare, can hardly be found among non-human animals."

Why is this so? Why are such constant features as war and mass murder found in human societies but not among any other species? This is likely the most important question confronting us as human beings.

The many forms of man's hostility to man are understandable if they are seen to be symptoms of a mechanism of adaptation run rampant. If you were alone in the wilderness and were set upon by a frightened or predatory animal, your life would depend largely upon the speed and effectiveness of your automatic fight and flight reflexes. These reflexes, so essential to man's survival in the cave and jungle, continue on through a sort of biological lag into our present experience, which is, of course, almost exclusively in civilized settings. These reflexes may be compared to other basically normal mechanisms of the body that also overshoot themselves. For instance, note the way in which body temperature rises to combat infections. It does so without any conscious directive on the part of the individual; this biological defense against disease simply rises automatically. But it may outstrip its controls, climbing to 106°, 107°, 108° and thus kill the individual before it kills the microorganisms against which it went into action. Similarly, the membranes of the nose and bronchial tubes swell and secrete juices in order to defend the body against irritants. But frequently they go too far in attempting to shut out dust, fumes, pollens, and the like, and hay fever or asthma may result. When severe enough, asthma may even cause death.

Observing animals closely, we find certain biological changes take place when danger threatens. Typical are the famous experiments conducted by physiologist Walter Cannon in 1928 and confirmed by many others since. Cannon, working in the early days of x-ray, mixed a little barium with a goose's food to make it opaque and then watched the stomach's reactions through a fluoroscope as the bird digested its meals under different conditions. The regular peristaltic movements of the esophagus were grossly disturbed by threats of danger such as a barking dog. Following this experiment, Cannon tested a variety of animals, including humans. Functional abnormalities showed up repeatedly whenever the animal was under stress. When threatened, the whole body's machinery goes into high gear: the blood flows from the viscera to the muscles; the heart pounds with greater force and increased speed; breathing is more rapid; the liver pours extra sugar as fuel into the blood. In this way the entire physiology prepares for extra action.

Exploring states of fear and rage in detail, Cannon found that, faced with any threat, frustration, or irritation, the animal becomes physiologically aroused for maximum effort—ready to fight or to flee. It is important to emphasize that while the two activities of fighting and fleeing appear quite different, inwardly the basic physiological preparations for them are essentially the same. The particular direction the resulting activity takes stems from the circumstances prevailing outside the animal, combined with his own inner needs, perception, and judgment. The carnivorous tiger, for instance, is aroused to *fight* when he senses the nearness of edible prey. The vegetarian rabbit, on the other hand, is aroused to *flee* when dangerous carnivores enter his territory. In the main, the rabbit's flight reaction is aroused mostly for defense while the tiger's fight response is mobilized for attack. Fight and flight thus represent two outcomes of a single physiological adaptive reaction. The one that prevails in action is largely a matter of expediency. If, for example, a mosquito attacks, you have no hesitation in striking to kill it. But if several hornets come at you, discretion would dictate that you use your aroused energies for flight, which you would doubtless find yourself doing automatically without consciously thinking about it.

Chapter 3

THE FIGHT-FLIGHT REFLEX AND PSYCHOLOGICAL ADAPTATION

Without doubt this fight-flight adaptive mechanism was vital for man in the earlier, more physically dangerous times of cave and jungle; it is today still valuable in primitive situations where the automatic mobilization for fight or flight can make the difference between life and death. But in the cooperative, civilized living of today, and in view of the moral, emotional, and intellectual problems (as opposed to physical perils) that confront most of us, this mechanism, when misunderstood and unrestrained is apt to outstrip its controls and be destructive to others and to oneself.

Until fairly recently, aroused, fearful, and courageous people could put an ocean safely between themselves and oppression, intolerance, and want. There were new frontiers; rich, arable land could be had for the tilling. Those who wished to do so could lose themselves among the lonely hills; and isolation from

mundane problems could be sought and found in monastic orders. But today, in most parts of the world, people who are frustrated, who are under stress, and even those who are in real political, social, or economic danger are barred by circumstances
and by the absence of vast open spaces from actual physical,
geographical flight and can only seek refuge in psychological
flight. This kind of flight may assume many different forms,
which for the sake of discussion we can arrange into four main
groups: sublimation and fantasy; use of drugs and intoxicants;
withdrawal states; and regressions. It should be noted here that
these groups are not intended to represent discrete categories of
psychological response. Rather, there is in fact considerable
overlapping in the behavior described under each form of flight.

It is quite normal and sometimes constructive for an individual under considerable stress to try and seek refuge by partici-
pating in earlier mental, emotional, and biological states
through sublimation and fantasy. This may be achieved in recreation, play, rest, or sleep. Some individuals, on the other hand,
find that by throwing themselves totally into their work they
gain an escape from emotional strain. Others may indulge in
fantasy, either through daydreaming or through creative expressions of their own or those readily accessible in fiction,
films, the theatre, painting, sculpture, and the like. The artist
handles his fantasies creatively, and he can combine an element
of escape with responsible productivity to make his way in the
world. The normal healthy person, if he does not use his fantasies professionally like the artist, is apt to take them in small
doses, as needed, and he is probably all the better for them.
There is nothing harmful in these activities of fantasy unless the
flight is extreme and prolonged, in which case there may be a
serious threat to the emotional health of the individual. For example, clinical experience reveals that early schizophrenia not
infrequently begins with addiction to movies and television.
Problems may also arise if hostility enters as a destructive element, as in the case of a game that becomes a gambling racket.

Intoxicants and drugs tempt the sorely pressed with promise
of quick surcease from the burdens of life. Many who feel as-
sailed by hardships from without and by emotional tensions

from within, find the relief experienced through tobacco, alcohol, and drugs to be irresistible. Unfortunately, the blessing is mixed; the addict seeks escape in vain. Eventually physical destruction comes, if it is not preceeded by emotional devastation.

Withdrawal states are a third form of escape. An extreme example of this is catatonia, a severe manifestation seen in schizophrenia. The patient is practically immobile and responds not at all to his surroundings and to other persons. If his arm, leg, head, or entire body is placed in a certain position, he will maintain this without change for prolonged periods.

A less severe form of withdrawal involves the giving up of all or nearly all responsibility. This may result from quite evident outsides pressures or the activating disturbance may come from within. Often the trend to withdraw is very strong because of early influences on the growing child, such as overprotection or deprivation. In such cases only slight pressures are enough to throw the individual into flight. For example, a seemingly responsible and industrious man begins to be unable to discharge his duties or pursue his regular routines. We learn that as a child he was severely overprotected. Although he has been able to make a go of life on his own thus far, he has done so under inner protest and with a persistent undercurrent of longing to return to the old responsibility-free days when he was entirely dependent upon others and had no one dependent upon him. No very hard knocks are necessary to initiate the flight reaction in such an individual. The psychological flight here may be expressed either in behavior alone, or it may emerge with an accompanying change in mood, such as depression or apathy.

Here is a more detailed example. James was subjected to excessive overprotection during childhood but he managed to fight his way free and assert a measure of independence. He married, had three children, and built a successful manufacturing business. To all appearances he was stably adjusted. But James was skating on thin ice. One day his partner suddenly withdrew from the business, deciding to retire to another city. James depended on this man, not only for the role he played in conducting the business, but emotionally. In fact, James never suspected just how much he relied on his partner, and the loss of the emotional support precipitated a withdrawal. He could no longer concentrate on work, and after a while he had enormous difficulty just getting up mornings. He witnessed with dismay the beginning of the ruin of his business and with it the loss of his family's security. He saw all this, but he was powerless to do anything by will alone to discharge his responsibilities. His mind and body simply withdrew; they refused to function. He was anxious rather than depressed. He was frightened, and realistically so, for this dangerous withdrawal seemed as much out of his conscious control as would be the raging fever of pneumonia. James was helpless to turn around the course of deteriorating events.

Withdrawal also plays an obvious part in most cases of depression, wherein the individual is apt to feel that life is no longer worthwhile. He loses interest in people and the outside world. Often physiological functions reflect this retreat by responding with a kind of clamping down of action—including constipation, diminished appetite for food and for sexual pleasure. In extreme form, depression can end in suicide, the ultimate withdrawal. The typical depression is a crystal-clear example of psychological flight combined with fight in the form of pent-up rage, which may be vented on the person himself, ultimately as suicide.

A fourth form of flight is regression. It has been found that various kinds of emotional disorders, whether occasioned by inner or outer tensions or some combination of both, are in large part returns to disturbed patterns of behavior that the individual had in infancy or childhood. Of course, this is seen in everyone to some degree. Just as most children, when they are injured physically or in their feelings, suck their thumbs or console themselves with sweets, so, too, many adults in trouble also turn to sweets, to food, or to drink. Some frightened children seek help dependently and submissively; many adults do the same. Some adults even turn back to the fight reaction which served them in childhood. A man may have learned mature ways of handling conflicts, but if in his childhood he met every irritation with attack, sufficient pressure and threats may revive this pattern in him and he may destroy his marriage and career.

The pressures that occasion a regression may be caused by an internal conflict that was initiated in childhood but which does not emerge until years later. A typical case is that of Bill. His mother was a high-powered and dynamic woman who was admired for her outstanding social and community activities. His father was an aggressive and successful businessman. Exposure to these parents imbued Bill not only with a drive to be successful, but also with an image of himself as a superior being, the son of superior parents. This kernel of vanity was fed directly by his parents' adoration of him. They projected upon him their own needs for superiority. And Bill, growing up in this emotional atmosphere, naturally absorbed their feelings and early developed an unusually strong image of himself as a superior individual.

In addition to this "narcissism," this vanity, egotism, and need for admiration, there was another trend that persisted with equal strength in Bill, namely, an excessive dependence on his parents. At the same time that they were adoring and attentive, his parents were also overly anxious about his every activity, and any sign of growing independence was greeted with resistance. It was all not too far from being perfectly normal in intention; it was just much too strong in the degree of its expression.

Not until he reached adolescence did Bill become definitely and acutely aware that something was severely wrong. He could not define it, but only sensed that he was different from other boys. At the core of the problem was his strong dependent love needs toward his parents and his feelings of being restricted. But he was not consciously aware of this. All Bill knew was that he felt weak and inferior to other boys, and to girls, too. Because of the narcissistic core in his personality, he found all these new feelings to be very confusing. His self-image was terribly hurt and threatened by this strange sense of weakness and inadequacy.

Bill reacted with inner rage, but what appeared on the surface was the flight part of the reflex mechanism. He became increasingly withdrawn until he was so regressed that he could no longer continue school. Before long, his competitiveness, the inevitable concomitant of his egoism, was defeated by seeing others going ahead while he was doing nothing and getting no-where. The final blow to his already severely shaken self-image came from being forced to recognize that something was seri-ously wrong with him mentally and emotionally. Bill was by this time twenty years old; after all these years of thinking of himself as superior and of being treated that way, he could not tolerate the thought of existence as an inferior, as a failure. He was not conscious of what was going on within himself and naturally felt that nothing could be done to correct it. Bill felt hopeless and thus became suicidal.

Regression is probably an essential element in all emotional disturbances. In phobias, for example, a person may undergo states of feeling similar to the insecurities characteristic of the small child when left alone. As an illustration of this we can note that the insecurity of the child learning to balance on his own two feet before taking his first steps, and his fears of being left alone are not unlike the fear of going out alone. Typically, the phobic overcomes these fears when another person is with him, just as a small child's anxiety is allayed by the presence of a par-ent or other trusted adult or friend. Hysterical behavior, such as uncontrolled weeping, laughter, temper, and the like, are usual-ly intelligible when viewed as a regression to the behavior of the child. The same connection is seen in those mercurial individu-als who amaze us with their radical shifts of mood, behaving like uninhibited children who by trifles are devastated one moment but delighted the next. In a compulsion neurosis, such as exces-sive handwashing, extreme care about dress, or the obsessive need to count everything, the abnormal behavior usually derives from training in cleanliness, manners, arithmetic, and so on. An adult may express the child's obedience to its parents through compulsive symptoms, while at the same time he is betraying his defiance by making a caricature of conscientiousness and con-formity in general by gross exaggeration.

Perversions also reflect psychological flight through regres-sion. In the case of perversions, this usually means a return to the sexual play or fantasies of childhood. Many people who have a neurotic or a psychopathic personality show quite frankly be-havior in which reason and mature judgment are all too much at the mercy of the emotions. This is the case and appropriately so early in life when the child's ego, with its grasp of reality, is still relatively undeveloped. In psychoses, of course, the regression is deeper and involves more disorder of the ego. Delusions of grandeur, for instance, bear a striking resemblance with childhood indulgence in make-believe. The hallucinations of schizophrenia become comprehensible as a return to the preverbal method of thinking in images, still utilized in our dreams.

Thus withdrawals and regressions are fundamental to the production of all the disorders that we recognize as addictions, psychoses, neuroses, and infantile behavior. And this form of flight is important in psychosomatic conditions also, where the wish to escape is not satisfied in reality and this causes disturbances in the physiology. For example, studies of persons with peptic ulcers suggest that in some cases the structural damage results from the individual's constant exposure to stressful situations from which he wishes, but is unable, to extricate himself. Reduced to its simplest terms it may be that the longing to escape is expressed through the stomach, which behaves as though it were always hungering for food. Biologically this reaction to emotional stress manifests itself as a disturbance in the functioning of the stomach (hyperactivity and hyperacidity), which in turn renders the organ more susceptible to injury. Other studies have shown that emotional forces also play an important role in essential hypertension. It would seem that persons who force themselves to carry responsibilities against powerful longings to withdraw and flee from such burdens, develop high blood pressure at least partially for this reason.

In all the emotional conditions that we have been discussing, regardless of how prominent the element of flight, there is always present at the same time the other side of the automatic adaptive mechanism, that is, the enormously powerful flight reaction. Hostility is thus inextricably fused to all forms of withdrawal, depression, manic episode, hysteria, phobia, compulsion, perversion, addiction, paranoia, schizophrenia, psychosomatic disorder, and the rest. Interestingly enough, psychiatry first explored and then continued to focus primarily on flight syndromes. Freud studied and described regression in detail, but, as we have noted, only toward the end of his life did he turn his attention to the importance of man's hostility. But even though he did come to recognize the portentous implications for humanity of unerotized aggression, his followers nevertheless continued to place the greatest emphasis on various forms of libidinal impulses. Even today, hostile drives have not been fully worked through clinically, theoretically, or in the practical training of analysts. Thus hostility remains less stressed, less clarified, less understood, and certainly not yet adequately appreciated for its fateful power. Always a cause, result, or concomitant of regression, hostility deserves at least parity of concern with libidinal impulses. In fact it is correct to say that the fight-flight reaction is an essential link or part of all emotional disorders, that is, of all psychopathology.

Unlike flight, actual fight is all too available an option to modern man, and because of the awesome power he can summon to serve this goal, it poses a far greater threat to survival. At one end of the scale it is expressed overtly as destructive aggression; at the other, it is expressed in a masked form under the guise of justice, righteousness, and love. It can be acted out, within or outside the law, by individuals acting on their own, by unorganized crowds or mobs, or by highly organized gangs or armies. It finds easy expression in crime, delinquency, oppression, rebellion, and warfare, the prevalence of which serves as an index of how widespread the problem is.

In the United States, for example, more than 6.5 million crimes are committed annually. Every hour, on the average, eighty-seven persons are robbed, beaten, stabbed, or shot. Last year there were more than 19,000 homicides (a 114 percent increase since 1960) and 51,000 forcible rapes (a 198 percent increase since 1960). The wars of the generation now in advanced chronological maturity killed more than 22 million and injured more than 35 million. Lesser, but no less pertinent, evidence of the fight reflex may be found in divorce statistics and in the astonishing increase in child abuse. All figures of this kind relating to war, crime, divorce, and battered children, however, only serve as crude guides to the overt expressions of hostility. What is not reflected here are the myriad emotional problems involving covert or indirect expressions of hostility that are aimed at the self or others. Last year alone there were more than 25,000 suicides in this country. And how many children and adults were injured psychologically by their own hostility or the hostility of others?

Alcoholics, for instance, in whom the escape and the destructiveness are obvious, number more than 6 million. Neurotics, who have been described colloquially as "fighting a civil war within themselves," add another 5 to 20 million. There are well over 2 million psychotics, with 1 million in institutions. Of course, there is some overlap in these statistics, but it is nevertheless clear that they run into the tens of millions and include a very sizable percentage of our population—probably a large majority.

Part Two

PSYCHOLOGICAL ORIENTATION

From childhood's hour I have not been
As others were—I have not seen
As others saw. . . .
Then—in my childhood—in the dawn
Of a most stormy life—was drawn
From every depth of good and ill
The mystery which binds me still.

EDGAR ALLAN POE

Chapter 4

SOURCE OF HOSTILITY

We have listed some results of hostility when this biological mechanism of adaptation, this fight-flight reaction, overshoots itself. The question then arises: Why does this mechanism, damaging as it is to us in our civilization, and threatening as it is to our very survival, continue to exist with such force?

The answer is at once simple and complex. Certainly hostility per se (except as the mechanism of adaptation we have described) is not inherited, or if it is, at present there is no scientific evidence whatsoever to support this. Nor is there evidence that any other form of neurosis is carried in the genes. Individual differences in talent and temperament are doubtless inherited to some extent, just as there are differences in body build and coloring. But there is only meager and uncertain evidence for heredity being of any appreciable weight in the etiology of emotional disorders (other than, possibly, some forms of psychosis). Hostility simply cannot be passed off as something we inherit and hence can do nothing about. The fact is that excessive hostility is a disease of personality, transmittable from person to person and from group to group, and basically, by contact from parents to children, from generation to generation.

It is true that from earliest recorded history we read of tribes, cities, and nations attacking others, stealing lands and movable wealth, taking as many slaves as they wished for cheap labor and for sexual purposes, and killing off all the rest to eliminate competition and the risks of retaliation. Then the fear of being themselves looted, pillaged, raped, murdered, and enslaved by other nations, led to constantly expanding frontiers. Rome pushed her boundaries further and further for both these reasons: to take the riches and to impose her peace.

And yet not all men in each nation yearned for aggressive pillage and murder; not all rulers were cruel tyrants. The hostility involved in robbing, murdering, and enslaving is not necessarily a general human characteristic, but rather an attribute of certain personalities. It is a matter of how readily corruptible the individual is. Indeed, if the major motivating forces in each of us could develop normally, without damaging interference or coercion from the outside, friendly, social cooperation would be the result. Only when this development is disturbed during the earliest formative years of infancy and childhood, by active mismanagement or by gross neglect (whether unconscious and well-meaning or conscious and willful) does the fight-flight reaction, with its resulting hostility, flower in full strength.

In contrast to the absence of evidence for hereditary factors in determining the intensity and status of hostility in different persons, the work done by ethologists and the clinical experience of dynamic psychiatry with children and adults show the significance of conditioning influences and their basic importance in causing vulnerabilities to external stresses and emotional disorders. (We are, of course, referring exclusively to physiologically healthy organisms and not to those suffering the effects of physical or chemical damage, deformity or impairment of the brain, glandular system, or other parts of the body; also excluded from our discussion are those having gross congenital developmental defects.)

Howard Lidell did some fascinating ethological studies with goats at the Cornell Animal Farm. In some of his most notable experiments he observed twin kids, one of whom Liddell isolated from its mother and placed alone in a room, which was identical to the one in which its mother and sibling remained. A few simple things are made to occur simultaneously in both rooms. For example, lights are flashed on and off and sudden sounds are made—nothing at all harmful is done. The kid that was allowed to remain with its mother becomes alarmed, rushes to its mother, and clings to her. The kid soon feels reassured and manages to adapt to the situation. The kid who is isolated from its mother panics at the flashing lights and sudden sounds, but he has no one to turn to for security. When this kid is reunited with its mother after a while, he reveals an incapacity to be mothered and reassured. The basic but delicate instinctual relationship, that elemental feeling normally existing between mother and child, has been disrupted. And the ramifications of this upset are enormous. The kid who could not get into the feelings of being mothered by its own mother also showed a striking inability to get into good feelings with any other animals. The relationship of the mother to its offspring serves as the model and pattern for future relationships. When this interplay of feeling is disrupted, the young cannot form future relationships with others in a normal way. The kid that had been isolated became, in essence, psychotic.

Ethologists have referred to this initial need of an offspring to cling to its mother as *imprinting*. In his revealing experiments, Eckhardt Hess has prevented ducklings from attaching their dependent love needs to their mother within the period of maximum imprinting, which in ducks is the first few days after hatching. The ducklings grow up unable forever after to relate to other ducks, socially or sexually.

Interference with the normal process of imprinting in humans also seems to lead to disastrous consequences. Rene Spitz has a remarkable film called *Grief—A Peril of Infancy*. It shows illegitimate babies with their own mothers. The children seem to be happy and thriving despite the often shabby environments in which they live. At age five months the children are placed in a foundling home where the facilities are excellent. The building is beautiful and the children are guaranteed a perfect diet and the best medical care. The physical surroundings are certainly better than the homes they came from. But of course in the foundling home there is no real mothering—no maternal love or consistent attention, affection, or play. With all the right food, medical attention, and lovely surroundings, the babies wilt. Some twist up as though suffering from a terrible disease of the nerves and muscles. Others become dangerously lethargic. All lose weight, and as many as 20 percent deteriorate until they die. These children fail to thrive because of ruptured imprinting or because their dependent love needs are starved.

The normal growth and development of the child who does not imprint properly or relate properly to its mother or substitute in the first months and years of life is seriously jeopardized. But so too is this the case for the child in whom the attachment does not yield a loving and secure image of its mother and father (or substitutes). The child's enormous plasticity and capacity for training, that is, its ability to be *conditioned*, is certainly one of the most outstanding characteristics of human beings.

The infant, in a very normal and natural way, craves love and security. If these needs are met whenever the mother appears, the child will come to associate the mother with feelings of satisfaction, love, and security. But if the appearance of the mother is associated with neglect or rejection, or with overprotection and domination, the child will become conditioned to this response. That is, the child will come to expect bad treatment and respond with fear and resentment. The fight-flight adaptive mechanism will be mobilized. As we noted earlier, this is the primitive but indispensible response of all animals to any and every threat to living out the life cycle. This is true whether the irritant comes from outside the organism or from within it, whether it is physical or psychological. The small child is in no position either to fight or to flee, and this situation of living and growing up under abuse that can neither be escaped nor destroyed, and that comes from a person upon whom the child is utterly dependent, generates chronic fear and rage. If the parent also loves the child, then the hostility usually causes guilt; and the child's primitive impulses to destroy the person upon whom he is so helplessly dependent typically create anxiety. The guilt and anxiety usually increase the child's clinging to the mother, who generally resents this and becomes even more rejecting. Thus a pattern of disordered feeling toward the mother is formed in the small child. The problem with a child who has been conditioned in this unfortunate way is that his negative response (in fact the whole emotional pattern) tends to spread to people other than his mother. And as such it constitutes a core of psychopathology.

Studies of sheep have helped us to understand how this phenomenon of conditioning and the spread of conditioned responses works. In one study, a sheep is brought repeatedly into a building where it undergoes a distressing experimental situation. It reacts not only against the specific situation, but also against the experimentor, the building as a whole, and even the adjacent fields. If the sheep is regularly kept in a nearby field, it is found to isolate itself from other sheep, to be hostile when approached by man or sheep, and to try frequently to escape. The antagonism to the experimental situation spreads to the animal's entire environmental surroundings and results in seriously disturbed personal relations with other sheep. This is not without parallels to what happens to the child who is subjected to early mistreatment. It reacts at first just against the parents, but then its resentment spreads to other individuals, and often even to society as a whole.

The human mind is powered by the biological processes of the body, by the effects of childhood conditioning, and by adaptive reactions to external circumstances, which always evolve to some degree from emotional needs. The extent to which the various motivations are subject to influence is a result of man's very long childhood as compared with the young of other species. This slow maturing gives him vast advantages over other animals but it also exposes him to greater dangers. Each person's drives and reactions are patterned by his first experiences and training, are given their main direction by the character and behavior of those who became the individual's first models. And the earlier the conditioning, the more potent its effects and the more likely that these effects will persist unchanged for life.

Each person has a certain picture of the world, of other people, of values, of himself. It is part of the way he understands reality, part of his conscious ego. Underlying this view, in the unconscious depths of his mind, is another picture that conforms more closely to the way things were first seen in childhood. What the individual's senses and his intellect tell him about reality are actually colored, if not grossly distorted, by composite images formed very early in experience. When the handling of the infant and young child helps its development to emotional maturity, it increases the natural capacity of the individual for responsibility, productivity, independence, and a clear sense of reality. It is these vital qualities that will develop the individual's capacity for social cooperation. But when conditioning influences impair the emotional development, disordered childhood reactions establish patterns that tend to persist as sources of irritation, frustration, and anxiety, and therefore hostility.

To understand how this works, let us look first at the structure of the personality. Our present concept is much like the old tripartite division: the mind is made up of reason, conscience, and animal impulses. Together these act out the inner drama of experience, with consciousness as the audience.

Grouped together under the term *ego* are: (1) the powers of perception gained through the senses, including the grasp of both outer reality and inner needs and urges; (2) the integrative powers of memory, reason, and the like; and (3) the executive functions of will, repression, and control. The ego is the conscious and most flexible part of the personality. It plans and coordinates action, is the essence of what we call the self, and acts as the great organ of adaptation to living with people. Without consciousness and its functions the individual would be helpless, only a vegetative organism.

The term *superego* includes those controls, models, and dictates that stand over the ego. It refers to all the effects of training, all the ideals and standards adopted from the family, personal experience, and cultural custom. It includes the conscience, the core of which is formed during the earliest weeks, months, and years of life. This core, though a powerful and enduring feature of the personality, is not static and entirely unalterable. Some changes in the effects of early conditioning result from the very process of living; others can be brought about through analytic treatment. The nucleus of the superego is probably the innate biological tendency of the mature organism toward social cooperation. Added to this are the effects of those who rear the infant and young child, the main characters in the drama of its early life. Because this core of the superego is formed so early, it is usually to a large extent automatic and unconscious and therefore much more powerful and much less reasonable than we would like to think. But this tendency of repeated actions and reactions to become automatic and often unconscious is not really unusual at all. To save psychic energy many everyday experiences are rendered automatic responses. For example, at first there is a considerable conscious struggle in learning to ride a bicycle or drive a stick-shift car, but in time we can do so automatically. In time our hands, feet, and eyes become perfectly coordinated without conscious thought on our part.

The animal impulses that develop out of the chemistry and physiology of our bodies are called the *id*, denoting their more impersonal nature. Drives for food, sex, love, mating, dependence, parenthood, competition, and the like involve the whole organism and are reflected in the mind. Our awareness of other drives fades out as they descend to lower levels of the nervous system. For example, we are not conscious of the reflexes that maintain our muscle tone, operate our liver, or contract our pupils against bright light. Thus the psychological, what is or can become conscious, merges into the subpsychological. It should be emphasized that mature drives, as well as infantile ones, are thoroughly part of the id. For example, mature sexual mating and parental drives are the mature id impulses, and the drives toward social living are probably extensions of these, or at least closely related to them. These drives are discernible in all mammalian species, with rare if any exceptions, and in most other species as well.

We are now in a position to focus upon the major motivational forces in the mind. They are rather limited in number. The endless variety of individual problems and symptoms result from different combinations of these few but powerful underlying motivations. They can be listed in shorthand form as: (1) dependence and the drive to independence; (2) needs to receive and to give love; (3) sex drive; (4) inferiority and egotism (narcissism); (5) competitiveness. Because of their enormous importance in any discussion about the source of hostility, we should also list here the most common symptoms that arise from disturbances of these basic motivations. These reactions would be, again in shorthand form: (1) fear and anxiety; (2) exaggerated hostility and guilt with withdrawal and regression; (3) disordered sexual feelings; (4) inferiority feelings; (5) a distorted sense of reality. These motivations and reactions combine in various degrees and proportions to produce the vast array of different personalities, forms of psychopathology, and symptoms.

The basic motivations, though discrete forces, are interrelated with one another. The infant is utterly helpless at birth and completely dependent upon its parents for survival. This dependence is distinguishable from but closely connected with its needs for their love. If such dependence and receptive needs for love become too strong, as they are apt to in overprotected or deprived children, they regularly give rise to feelings of inferiority. As the child grows it comes to feel ashamed of being dependent on another. The resultant feelings of inferiority intensify egotism, envy, and competitiveness. Thus the weakness causes shame, and the concomitant hostility causes guilt; both guilt and shame are reactions of the superego, which includes the conscience and standards.

Sexual feelings may be disordered directly by excessive repression or by overstimulation during childhood. And anxiety may be cultivated in the child by an overanxious parent. But these, then, are essentially the effects of something wrong in the superego, that is, in the reactions that the individual has taken over from the parent and from the mores of society. Disturbance in the sense of reality is also a symptom rather than a force, but it is of special importance. All emotional disorders represent an excessive persistence of or regression to disordered infantile emotional patterns. The disorders may be classified as either internal or as reactive to later stress upon emotional vulnerabilities, which are determined by these patterns of childhood.

The major sources of hostility are the result of disturbances in the normal maturing of these motivations. In the next chapter we will trace in some detail how disorders of the motivational forces lead to mobilization of the fight-flight mechanism and then to psychological expressions of hostility.

Chapter 5

HOSTILITY AS PSYCHOPATHOLOGY

The central importance of the child's dependence upon the parents and the exceedingly long period of that dependence (as compared with other species) is a basic factor in the development of neurotic disorders. There is probably always in the adult some of the child's emotional dependence, but what is important is how much of this persists and how it is dealt with. One of the most striking features in the development of the human personality and mind is the interplay of progressive and regressive forces. The progressive forces involve the organism's move to maturation from parasitic dependence upon the mother; it is a move toward independence in caring for itself, in reproducing, and in being capable of caring for others. This progressive trend is always in conflict with an opposite, regressive tendency whereby the individual moves from later, more mature patterns back toward earlier, less developed ones.

The child's drive toward independence from the parents is a basic force in the young of all species. At birth the infant breathes for itself. Before long it can take solid food in by mouth instead of being dependent on the mother's milk. With strength and coordination it begins to walk and do things for itself. With curiosity it learns about the world and develops judgment. Then finally, when full size is reached, the energies toward growth and independence overflow into activities of mating, parenthood, and social productivity. From being parasitic, the individual becomes parental. It is this capacity for self-reliance and for the care of others that gives the mature adult his strength, his sense of security. And only with this kind of independence comes real social maturity—interdependence.

However, in conflict with this progressive drive there is also present a counterforce, the tendency to be fixated at or to regress to childish dependence. The drives to maturity must conquer the pleasures of being babied. Sometimes it is overprotection that impedes growth to self-reliance; sometimes, on the other hand, being forced to independence too early causes an aversion to it. Either way, parents who interfere with the normal progressive development make an adult who, however powerful physically and intellectually, still craves a support that he never outgrew the need for. Such cravings, of course, can rarely be gratified in life. Few adults get from mates, colleagues, or friends the treatment they had or wanted to have as children from their parents. Also, because the underlying needs to be dependent are usually in sharp contrast with the wish to be mature, they are apt to cause an inner sense of weakness and inadequacy which, in turn, insults the self-esteem and leads to reactions of rage.

For example, let us note the case of Charles, a young student who became so intensely hostile that he was unable to get along with his professors or classmates. He began to have ideas that everyone was against him. This led him to break off with his girlfriend, whom he had been dating regularly for more than a year. Finally he became so upset that he had to leave college. He managed to find a job, but soon discovered that his old troubles persisted. It turned out that for as long as he could remember he had been pampered by his mother and older sister. Charles's parents had been divorced, and the two women who were responsible for raising him centered all their interest and attention on him. They praised his slightest achievement and cushioned his every hurt. Thus, when the time came for him to move away from home and go to college, he felt that he could not exist without them and was angered when they insisted that he try. Moreover, his sense of dependence, which he was not consciously aware of, made him feel inferior to his contemporaries and this enraged him because of the threat it posed to his self-esteem. While away from home, Charles's fight-flight reaction was kept constantly aroused by the frustration of his desires for dependence on his mother and sister and by his protest against being independent and having to assume responsibilities. His hostility was forcing him into paranoia; that is, he projected his own rage onto others and felt that they were hostile and persecutory toward himself.

Following is a more detailed clinical vignette presenting a young criminal and sexual delinquent. The case of Paul is particularly interesting for a number of reasons. First, it provides a contrasting example to Charles, the young student just mentioned. The case of Paul shows what can happen when the hostility arising from feelings of excessive dependence is turned outward against others. Secondly, the dynamics in this case present in very clear terms the interrelationships of all the major motivational forces. As such, this vignette will supply insights for the discussion later in this chapter on how disorders of the basic motivations lead to psychopathological expressions of hostility.

Paul, twenty-one years old, was referred for psychiatric treatment while under indictment for burglary. He was the youngest son of a well-to-do, middle-class family. He was attractive, of superior intelligence, and in excellent condition physically. His father held a responsible position in a large manufacturing company. His brother, two years older, was working. His sister, six years older, was married. The mother took care of the home, which was comfortably appointed and desirably located. The family history was psychiatrically negative on the father's side, but there was a suicide and a few nervous breakdowns on the mother's side. So far as was determined, Paul's developmental history was normal and uneventful throughout the pregnancy and early years with two notable exceptions, namely, finickiness about food and temper tantrums. In contrast to this infantile behavior was an almost compulsive desire to be stronger than his brother—a factor that gives a clue to Paul's whole impulse-ridden character. The exaggerated competitive demand to be strong, later to be tough, was a reaction against his exaggerated needs for dependence.

Paul's major difficulties began at about the time he entered high school. He was dismissed from one school after another because of unruliness, drinking, and exposing himself to girls. The discipline of a series of military academies also failed to socialize his behavior. He nevertheless somehow succeeded in finishing high school and in being accepted by a college. He was again expelled on the same charges of unruliness, drinking, and indecent exposure. It is interesting to note here that during his psychiatric treatment Paul denied these charges, with the exception of admitting to some instances of rebellion against authority. He would either deny the dismissals from school outright, or he would claim that they were due to low grades. Actually his conversation, work, and intelligence tests all showed him to be a boy of superior intelligence.

Paul's difficulties repeated themselves according to their stereotyped pattern in his job, in his relationships with girls, and in all of his social encounters. His life was, so to speak, lived for him by unconscious forces that he could not control. Thus in the jobs that he was occasionally able to get, he would be insubordinate and rebellious while at the same time demanding higher wages, thus assuring his dismissal. His pattern toward a date was to pick a fight with the girl and then refrain from any gesture of reconciliation. This behavior was designed to prove his independence of her. So prominent was the denial of the dependent element in the relationship that, although he would provoke the quarrel, he considered that any friendly step on his part would be a show of weakness.

A survey of Paul's behavior in general social relationships showed the same pattern: bravado and toughness as a front to hide from himself and the world his core of softness and weakness, his exaggerated dependence upon others for shelter and subsistence. Thus in place of constructive work of value to himself and to others, at school or in his jobs, Paul overslept, overate, drank to excess, gambled, stole, and in general defied all authority. At the same time he was supported by his family, whom he practically blackmailed by his behavior. Sexually, he did not love, but only peeped and exhibited himself.

Such delinquent behavior netted him a court record of four arrests in the five years prior to his coming for psychiatric treatment. The various charges included indecent exposure, larceny, disorderly conduct (peeping in windows), and burglary. He was seen by the court psychiatrist, who made a diagnosis of "psychopathic personality—not committable as insane or feebleminded." The prognosis being very poor for any improvement without radical changes in his personality, he was given a choice between jail and psychiatric treatment during parole. Although he chose treatment, it later came out that his soft dependent core actually yearned for the irresponsible life of jail, where he could be entirely dependent, supported without effort, and secure. Also, being in jail would allow him to see himself as a tough guy, an image he longed to assume.

Throughout the analysis, Paul never mentioned his perversions, exhibitionism, and peeping, and much of what he did tell about was probably touched up by his imagination. At one point rather early on in treatment he was frank enough to say that he could not face his own soul, that he would go only so far and no further. Nevertheless he did cooperate to a large extent in free associating and thus revealed the problems that his pride and fear resisted seeing but that deep down he timidly wanted to face and solve.

In practically everything he said or did, the soft-tough conflict was apparent. The affectations of his appearance (the enormous belt, the garish shirts, heavy shoes), the swagger, the jaunty cigarette always dangling, the sophisticated air, were all quite transparent. Beneath this veneer was the attractive smile and naive, even sweet expression of a very little boy, frightened and appealing. So, too, in the analysis the defiant delinquent toughness was only a front for what showed clearly beneath—namely, the soft core, the not yet outgrown infantile passive, receptive dependent needs.

These conflicting attitudes were traceable back to his infancy in an almost unaltered pattern. It went as follows: Paul's strong wish to be dependent caused him to feel weak and inferior in comparison with other men. This, in turn, impelled him to prove that he was the opposite, that is, strong and independent. Thus he was in a constant struggle to satisfy these conflicting desires —to be as dependent and receptive as a child, and yet also to be as independent as a man. It is therefore of considerable interest that his mother, when questioned as to Paul's earliest behavior in infancy, told that before the boy was a year old and until he was about five years of age, he had recurrent temper tantrums. These episodes of rage would be terminated only when his mother picked him up and carried him. In this way Paul not only vented his anger, but also dominated his mother. Moreover, the mother told, from the time of his very earliest activity, he showed an intense desire to be stronger than his older brother. So Paul's first behavior of which we have record shows efforts at domination and willfulness toward his mother. The purpose of this display of independent will, however, was entirely dependent: to get himself carried. This dependent need made him feel weak in comparison with his brother and so he tried constantly to prove that he was stronger.

The extent to which this pattern persisted is shown by the patient's statement during treatment that he always feared only two things: to be humiliated by a woman and to meet a man in his own field. Paul's feelings of weakness were so overpowering that he constantly sought to prove his superiority. He could not stand competition with a man if there was a chance of losing. Therefore, he would never compete with his brother or, transferring this pattern, with other boys in the common field of scholarship, sports, and, later, business. (He once lost at squash before a small audience and became so furious that he wanted to attack his victorious opponent physically. He never played the game again.) So instead of competing normally, Paul tried to make himself expert in gambling, drinking, and stealing. Thus the trend toward criminality developed out of the need to show his toughness and superiority, which he felt he could not do in normal competition because of his infantile, receptive dependent demands. True to the pattern, the surface show of strength and independence was in reality a flight away from these.

The early finickiness about food showed the same earmark and persisted in full force in adulthood. Paul felt he had to be the boss and in the interest of achieving this end he tyrannized his family, especially his mother, so that he could eat when and what he pleased. This trend was connected with his later drinking, which he regarded not as a pleasurable indulgence and escape, but as a manifestation of toughness.

This receptive conflict was very clear in relation to Paul's family. Coupled with extreme demands upon his mother, especially in regard to food, and rage at the slightest thwarting, was a feeling that he could not stand to receive anything from her. Similarly he demanded money from his father (whom he strongly preferred to his mother), and yet he could hardly stand to accept it. Paul would rather have stolen than have been financially dependent on his father. So strong was this feeling that he could not endure indebtedness to anyone and never expressed gratitude to anyone for anything. Toward his brother, beneath the active competition, was an intense envy of any attention the brother received. This same trend filled him with a bitter hatred of women, because he saw them as people who can be supported and can be frankly receptive—something he could never be. With a girlfriend, as we mentioned earlier, he would try to show his strength by denying his dependence.

Outside of the family the conflict repeated itself with great precision. In school and at work Paul asserted his independence, but only in order to demand privileges and escape responsibilities. Gambling was thrilling because of the anticipation of easy money—and he had little to lose, for he used other people's money. Horse racing provided the same daydreams plus the thrill of identifying with the competing horses. In stealing and holdups, too, Paul could play the strong, dominant man and yet get something for nothing, without feeling inferior, dependent, and obligated. Eventually, however, this came to involve not only risk, but initiative, when he landed a job with an underworld gang. He was hired to drive trucks, and at first this had great appeal for Paul. But then came the problems of competing with other men, and so Paul never got too deeply involved with organized crime. Instead, he just hovered on the edge of the underworld.

In the sexual sphere his reactions were no different. Paul would pick up girls as a show of masculinity. He never mentioned the exhibitionism and peeping in the analysis because it was too patently infantile, too close to the soft core. His typical mechanism was again clearly demonstrated by the circumstances of his last arrest. The police were summoned because Paul was seen peeping in some windows. When he was apprehended he admitted to attempted burglary, not to peeping. He could boast of criminality to deny a sexual perversion, which was a clear attempt to hide the soft core by what seemed a more masculine front. All perversions are infantile fixations, childish impulses that have not been outgrown, and there is little doubt that in this case the peeping, like all the other behavior, was a manifestation of this boy's almost stereotyped pattern—namely, a receptive wish overlaid by a pseudomasculine attack. Unable to perform the adult masculine act, the peeping served as a substitute for it. Paul's sexual perversions were in essence manifestations of the same conflict that was so apparent in the other spheres of his life.

Paul's failure to compete and feelings of inferiority together with his unsatisfiable needs for dependence and independence, filled him with rage and defiance, and this persistently hostile attitude made him constantly guilty and fearful of retaliation. Much of the bravado was itself a denial of his fears. He dared not relax. No wonder then that he ran away from home, from school, from jobs, where his emotions made human contacts so painful. It is also not surprising that he even welcomed the idea of prison, where he need not compete, where his conscience could be appeased, and where he could indulge his desires to be dependent. That attraction to prison was the reason for his laconic, detached, schizoid attitude when the judge threatened him with commitment for life. Paul reported that when he heard the judge say that, he could hardly keep from laughing in the man's face.

Dependence and needs for love are closely intertwined, but they are not identical. The child's need for physical care must be distinguished from his clamorous demands for attention and coddling. For the child, being loved is the guaranty of being cared for and protected, the assurance of survival. Being loved is the libidinal component of dependence. Adults with mature needs for love fulfill these by giving responsible love and by being loved in return. But they are reconciled to the fact that no one ever receives all the love that he wants. Persons in whom childish needs for love remain too strong may be incapable of this realistic adaptation to experience and thus go to desperate extremes to get attention directly.

The roots of such patterns go deep into infancy. Sometimes the inherent needs for love were disturbed in childhood by being threatened, frustrated, or otherwise injured; sometimes they were overindulged; sometimes the behavior necessary to get love is warped by excessive demands on the part of the parents. For example, one patient, a personable young man, was reared to get love only by being entirely submissive to a tyrannical father. He grew up with this submissiveness, but hated himself for thus thwarting his masculine independent drives. He went through life feeling that he must always be submissive, yet inwardly he raged against this.

All people grow up unconsciously feeling that they can win love only if they behave as they had to behave in childhood to win it. Thus the hunger for love, which is so central a motivational force, causes other patterns of behavior to shape themselves to gratify it. This powerful need can give rise to a variety of emotional problems not only by molding these other patterns, but also through abnormalities in itself of kind and degree.

Some people, though they are independent in their judgment and actions, and though they betray no need to lean upon others, are yet tormented by cravings for love that are so intense as to be virtually insatiable. Normally as the child grows to maturity there is a gradual diminution in the intensity of the need to receive love and an increase in the enjoyment of giving love. Deprivation and overindulgence are two of the common errors of upbringing that disturb the normal give-get balance. If the emotional diet in childhood is too rich or too poor, then the appetite for love later in life is exaggerated or otherwise disordered.

Cravings for love, like other emotional forces, are more or less readily displaced or redirected away from the parents to other people and objects. When they are excessive and disordered, they may form the nucleus of an addiction. In such extreme cases, the cravings are tenaciously fixed onto other persons (often as infatuations), or onto objects, such as food (as in bulimia, which is pathologically increased appetite) or money (as in avarice) in the vain hope that the insatiable childhood need for love will be satisfied.

Betty, an extremely capable young female executive, had the intelligence and good looks to set her well on the road to success. Instead of being happy and enjoying herself, she was hostile and chronically depressed. At the office she made no close friends among women, and outside the office she established the most intense attachments to men. Repeatedly she would fall so deeply in love that she would become almost unable to work; yet these affairs invariably ended in violent quarrels. As a child Betty never received adequate love from her mother, who was too busy with a very active social life to give much attention to her daughter. Desperately, Betty turned to her father. Though she clung to him, he was not around enough to satisfy her needs because his work demanded that he travel a great deal. As a substitute for himself and his love, Betty's father offered her an endless stream of lavish gifts as compensation. Now that she was grown, Betty could neither feel comfortable with members of her own sex nor could her young male friends match her father's fantastic gifts. Because of her excessive demands, she would lose her boyfriends and then become furious at everyone. At times she became depressed to the point of suicide.

Like exaggerated dependent needs, the child's desires for love, especially when heightened by fear, frustration, spoiling, and other faults in upbringing, cannot be gratified in adult life. Inevitably thwarted, they form a source of constant irritation, leading to a sense of hopelessness and failure, to all varieties of neurotic symptoms, including, always, irrational rage.

A case in point is that of Alice, a fifteen-year-old girl who is currently at a rehabilitation institution for juvenile delinquents. She has been there for about a year. At the age of thirteen she was arrested and charged with disorderly conduct, resisting arrest, assault and battery on an officer, and damage to city property. Just six months prior to this incident she was arrested and charged with assault with intent to kill—for serving poison to her mother. Alice denied this charge, saying that some Draino accidentally fell into her mother's coffee cup and that she didn't mean for it to happen. Alice has actually been known to the courts almost since her birth because of recurrent custody problems.

Her parents are both heavy drinkers who have constantly been involved in illicit sexual relationships with a grotesque constituency of paramours. Alice has three brothers: Robert is a year older than she and is now at a juvenile correctional facility because of generally incorrigible and criminal behavior; Steven is a year younger than Alice and now lives in a foster home; Michael is just three years old and lives at home. This youngest boy was born of one of the mother's paramour relationships.

Alice's parents have a long history of separation and reconciliation; the mother has moved many different times with the children, usually to new neighborhoods. When the family is together, the mother and father drink excessively and fight most of the time. In fact, Alice's earliest memory is of her mother and father fighting. Alice recalls that she and her brothers, Robert and Steven, were always trying to push the father away so he wouldn't pummel the mother with his powerful fists. Alice reported that she had frequent fights with these two brothers and that when they would make up they would all agree, "Let's love each other and not be like mother and father."

Because of the drinking and the paramours, neither of Alice's parents ever had much time for her or the boys. The children were left alone a great deal and were usually dirty, ill-nourished, poorly clothed, inadequately supervised, and in various other ways severely neglected. For a few years, until she was about ten or eleven, Alice used to wait up at night for her mother to come home. The woman would stagger in drunk and Alice would make her some food and put her to bed. She would carefully tuck her mother in so that she wouldn't, in her stupor, fall onto the floor. The woman is large and husky, and sometimes when drunk she would mercilessly beat her daughter. Alice says she never fought back because she felt her mother did not know what she was doing and that it wasn't right to hit her.

The father made a final break with the family, deserting them when Alice was ten. The mother then took her children and moved to a very tough neighborhood, where the children had to learn to fight to protect themselves. Very quickly they mastered the necessary skills for survival. The mother got a job as a barmaid, but her drinking soon cost her the job. To get money the children took to stealing. They were caught and placed in a detention center. Alice kept running away, always returning to her mother only to find the woman completely wrapped up in one lover or another.

Alice has been placed previously in two foster homes. She could not sustain the first placement, becoming very demanding of attention through negative behavior. She proved unable to live within the limits of a normal home environment. She was exceedingly defiant and accepted few directions from figures of authority. When she became agitated, which was much of the time, she would listen to no one and refuse to take responsibility for her own behavior and feelings. In the second home she did receive the attention she demanded but it did not seem to be enough for Alice. Her school situation deteriorated considerably during this period. She developed no peer relationships and fought with everyone, including teachers who countered her need to have her own way. She often appeared as a very spoiled, demanding child with a violent temper. Just as she had run away from the detention center, so too she fled these foster homes, always returning to her mother. Alice wanted desperately for her mother to become a devoted, caring parent.

When she was eleven Alice became pregnant for the first time. She claims that a boy threatened to hurt her if she didn't have intercourse with him, so she yielded. Alice became pregnant but aborted by going with her brothers to a vacant lot where she convinced them to jump up and down on her abdomen. A year later Alice was raped by one of her mother's boyfriends. Again she became pregnant, but this time she had a spontaneous miscarriage.

A year later Alice was charged with attempting to kill her mother by poisoning. She was adjudicated delinquent and committed to a correctional facility for juveniles. While there she discovered that she was pregnant. Alice again acted out, becoming abusive to the staff, generally hostile toward the other inmates, and excessively demanding of all who came in contact with her. Finally, she succeeded in running away. She returned to live with her mother and was allowed to stay there. Not long after returning home Alice prematurely delivered a baby boy, and it was during her hospital stay that she resumed her outbursts of violence. The baby, considerably underweight, remained hospitalized for two months after which time he was discharged to Alice and her mother. They both refused placement for the baby. In fact, Alice threatened suicide if either one of them were placed.

Though she officially returned to live with her mother, Alice spent extended periods away from home. While her mother seemed only superficially concerned, she refused to keep custody of Alice and the baby if this continued. Nevertheless, the girl persisted in her periodic disappearances and her mother finally filed a police report. Soon thereafter Alice tried to commit suicide by taking an overdose of pills. When she returned home she claimed that she had been staying with a boy and that she tried suicide because he had thrown her out. At that point, Alice's mother requested that her daughter be placed. Alice became distraught, insisting that she remain with her baby. She convinced her mother that she would kill herself, and the woman finally changed her mind and agreed to allow Alice and the baby to remain with her. Three months later the baby was found dead, having fallen from a second story window. Alice was accused of killing him and she was then placed in a youth detention center. After a homicide investigation, the death was ruled accidental as there was insufficient evidence to prove otherwise. While at the center Alice continued to get into fights with the other girls and to physically abuse the supervisor. She showed a complete lack of control over her temper and was easily provoked.

It is apparent that Alice is even now quite lonely and still longs for a positive relationship with her rejecting mother. Alice is an insecure, inadequate youngster who has a tremendous need to act out aggressively and violently. She tries to defend against the chronic anticipation of rejection by her exceedingly oppositional behavior, which in reality camouflages some very deep-rooted needs for nurturance. These needs are exaggerated and disordered by the fact that Alice has never been able to receive nurturance from the dominant authority figures in her environment. Although she still yearns deeply for her mother's love and attention, she sees the woman as a rejecting, punitive, and destructive person who has caused her great conflict.

Alice's evasiveness, cunning, and hostile acting out are all methods of compensation that bring her attention, recognition, and in some distorted way, acceptance by other people. During her most recent psychiatric interview it was noted that Alice is developing a great deal of paranoid ideation. Alice is daily becoming more fantasy oriented and fixated on the need for nurturance. All frustrations and threats stimulate the fight-flight reaction with its hostility. Alice had more than her share of frustrations and fears; and with such conditioning, so consistently and almost from birth, the chances of her changing or outgrowing these pathological patterns through any form of therapy are negligible. The twig has been too severely bent ever to grow into a straight tree.

Let us now turn to a consideration of another very powerful source of hostility: inferiority feelings and the drive for power. In most cases this begins with the little child's feelings of weakness in comparison with his parents. Normally this is balanced in the child by the assurance that, though smaller, he is essentially like his parents and in time will become their equal. Assuming there is no disturbance in development, the child will pass through adolescence and reach his full powers as an adult some time later on. He will come to feel secure and find maturity through identification and a capacity to empathize with the mature members of his family, with friends, and with co-workers. The satisfactions gained through the mature use of these adult powers come to yield more enjoyment and pleasure than the earlier self-centered ones that characterized the child's helplessness, weakness, and impotence.

If an individual has been reared in such a way that he retains into adulthood too much of the attitudes of childhood, he will continue to feel small, dominated, and inferior. In such a person the pattern of still being a child in a world of adults persists in his feelings. Consequently, he is constantly driven to prove his worth, to seek all sorts of compensation—or else, of course, he may give up the struggle altogether. This disturbed development, like the other forms we have discussed, is felt by the individual, although not understood by him, as a serious threat to the self and thus gives rise to the fight-flight reaction with its feelings of rage and hostility.

Sometimes the need for prestige that underlies the sense of inferiority is directly fostered by the parents: a child may be conditioned to expect their love only when he achieves some sort of outside recognition. Much of the competitiveness between adults has its roots in the early inculcated and prolonged striving for good grades, athletic distinction, or popularity. Such a basis for the giving or withholding of affection intensifies natural envy between brothers and sisters and also the rivalry inherent in a child's relations with a parent of the same or opposite sex. Of course, a certain amount of competition is useful in growth, but when childish competitiveness is prolonged or overemphasized, it is apt to cause ceaseless, compulsive striving and bitter envy. Obviously this will destroy good feelings and good relations within the family and generate outside hatreds, which usually persist through later life.

Adults crippled by their failure to outgrow inflated demands for prestige become filled with chronic hostility. And it is this emotional force that underlies the struggle to keep up with the Joneses, to beat out the other fellow. Strength and teamwork are mistranslated into serving a battle for personal status. These exaggerated needs are a corrupting influence on human values, on the system of ideals that allows men to live together in community. The survival and happiness of a society depends on how much each member contributes, not upon how much each member takes out.

Closely related to the needs for prestige and status is the drive for power. Before his sense of reality is fully developed, the very young infant goes through what has been called "a stage of omnipotence." When the infant's needs are satisfied as soon as they arise and in an almost automatic fashion, the responsive parents appear at first to be mere extensions of its wishes, cries, or gestures. This period, if unduly prolonged, may condition children to the feeling that they must only want something to have willing slaves ready to satisfy them.

Power is the individual's great assurance that his own needs can be satisfied in spite of all. Whether an adult seeks power in order to make a constructive contribution to humanity or whether he seeks it only to satisfy inner personal needs is a test of emotional security and maturity. Power drives can take many forms—muscular prowess, sexual potency, the ability to compel obedience, sheer physical domination over another. The important issue is how this power is used. It can be directed toward mature and humanely beneficial purposes associated with protecting and providing for the family and community, regardless of how broadly this latter term is interpreted. Or, at the other end of the spectrum, it can be utilized for purposes of exploitation and brutality.

At the very core of both excessive power drives and exaggerated demands for prestige are usually feelings of inferiority, which in greater or lesser degree seem to harass an amazing number of people in our civilization. Disguises for these feelings are generally unsuccessful; it takes no particularly astute observer to recognize that beneath most inflated egos lies insecurity. Put generally, feelings of inferiority usually result from actual emotional inferiorities that are representative of failures of parts of the individual to develop fully to emotional maturity. Desires for power, a sense of inferiority, egocentricity, failure of human sympathy—these are the cardinal characteristics of the hostile mind. They are most obvious in the ruthless spouse and parent, the political tyrant, the merciless criminal. All these people share a deficiency in identification with other individuals (that is, an inability to see and empathize with others as human beings like themselves); they react to others only as objects of their own hostile and frequently sadistic lusts.

The various distorting forces that warp the mind of the infant or child for life may be subtle or they may come into the open as direct cruelty and even violence. Whatever their nature—overprotection, neglect, inconsistent training, excessive ideals, debased standards, seductiveness, exploitation—whether stemming from the parents' misguided love or conscious sadism, the result is some form of crippling of the emotional life. The impairment may be in any or all parts of the personality. It may be primarily a reaction of the id (for example, excessive dependence upon one or the other parent), or it may lie in a disorder of the superego (for example, in guilt, in harshness of conscience, in false standards, in continually reaching for ideals that are so high as to be impossible of fulfillment). Simply the lack of good loving persons with whom to identify during earliest years of childhood can also be a cause of emotional crippling, for this may result in a poor sense of reality and poor control over the impulses. These reactions to the parents' treatment of the child become traits of the child's personality and as such form the foundation for the individual's reactions to other persons. This core pattern of response persists for life. From the point of view of psychopathology it is always a question of degree, a question of the intensity of the emotional forces and the balance that results among all of them in their interactions.

Whatever the specific nature of the personality deformity, the resulting sense of inferiority is usually reacted against violently. It is an intolerable internal irritant and a threat to the individual's security. It is so widespread a problem that it would be impossible to list briefly all the ways in which different individuals react to it. We have mentioned some in discussing needs for power and for prestige. All the reactions, however, regardless of the specific form they may assume, have one powerful element in common: hostility.

A man feels a nameless, indefinable inferiority, which he may not even admit to himself. He cannot come to grips with its sources. He may try to change but the core of his personality is actually unknown to him and is probably so fixed that, without analytic treatment or unusual experiences, he is unable to do anything about it. He is threatened but he cannot change, he cannot flee and he cannot fight the threat itself. He is blind to his inner unknown assailant and the result is what has been aptly termed *impotent rage*. Irritated and threatened from within, the individual generates a constant pressure of rage and hostility that can come out against the strong, whom he bitterly envies, or against the weak, who remind him of his own inferiority.

Douglas has spent nine of the last ten years in a federal penitentiary. He is now twenty-eight years old and serving a sentence for manslaughter. Four years ago, while confined to a maximum security cell, he attempted suicide. This uncontrollably hostile young man is the youngest of five brothers, three of whom are now serving time in prison for various crimes of violence. The fourth brother was killed two years ago, while on parole, in a shoot-out in a local bar. Douglas's childhood was marked by severe hostilizing experiences. In fact, his earliest memory is of the police coming to arrest his oldest brother. When his parents refused to admit the officers, the door was broken down and the brother seized. The father viciously attacked the police, who nevertheless succeeded in dragging the boy off.

In describing his early years, Douglas rather mournfully notes that he always felt rejected and ignored by his father, whom he believes has always favored his other brothers. In all he says about his family it is clear that Douglas has never had a relationship of loyalty and trust with either his parents or any of his brothers. His mother regularly and unfairly beat Douglas with a stick several times a week. There were numerous fights between Douglas and his father, especially when the man was drunk.

Apparently this was quite often as he had developed a serious drinking problem over the years. Douglas, even as a very young boy, knew that his father saw other women and that his mother saw other men. In fact his mother would become exceedingly promiscuous whenever Douglas's father was away in prison. And this, too, was not an infrequent occurrence. There is little evidence of family loyalty.

Douglas was a severe disciplinary problem in school and was constantly being suspended for misbehavior (mainly for fighting with classmates). He recalls being tauntingly called "jailbird" by the other students because of his father's and brothers' prison records. Douglas dropped out of school when he was sixteen and soon thereafter was arrested for aggravated assault and battery. He had viciously attacked a black man in movie theater because, as he later explained to the judge, "I didn't like his looks." This seemed to Douglas to be an adequate motive, even though he almost killed his victim.

Apparently blacks are a chief target of Douglas's hostility. While in prison he struggles with only modest success to control his enormous hatred of them. When asked about his feelings toward blacks he replied that he just hates them "in general—the way they act, the way they treat other people, the way they control the prisons. Why, they rape us white people! I'd like to kill 'em, kill 'em all!" Black prisoners are not his only target. He claims that all the officers and guards in the prison treat him unfairly. Douglas believes they are jealous of his ability to control the other inmates—the white ones, that is. He detests the prison personnel because he feels they should keep the black prisoners segregated from the white ones.

Douglas describes pervasive feelings of being inferior and of being exploited by others. Vicious, powerful, and narcissistic hostility is his only defense. He is frustrated, enraged, and depressed about the future, and seems constantly perplexed by the enormous difficulty he experiences in controlling his behavior. Because of his very strong tendency to project the responsibility for his actions onto others, he cannot come to any real understanding about his own motivations.

In the case of Douglas we can see a young man who was severely traumatized by his hostile, disloyal, rejecting parents. His childhood experiences resulted in excessive feelings of inferiority and worthlessness. When he attempts to deny these feelings he does so through displays of hostile, dominating, and violent behavior. He has a pathological quantity and intensity of hostile feelings and an equally pathological lack of control over his behavior.

It is because of the high proportion of individuals filled with feelings of inferiority and with reactions to it of pride, power seeking, and hostility that we have so many of this world's problems. What engenders so much of the anxiety, pain, and suffering between nations, within nations, in families, in business organizations, and even in professional societies is the pride and hate that drive men who think they know better than other men, the men who ruthlessly impose their will with little capacity for sympathetic understanding. Yet, despite their power, these men are usually emotional cripples who have failed to develop a mature capacity to give and to receive love. The person who shows exaggerated egotism, need for power, and, above all, hostility is suffering from a serious emotional disease. He is psychopathological, and it is of immense practical importance that this be recognized.

The superego, of which the conscience is a part, is largely a product of conditioning. Essentially it is a precipitate of training attitudes that have clustered about the nucleus of the individual's natural instinct toward social living. As we noted earlier, this instinct for social cooperation is a common feature seen throughout the animal kingdom. The conscience of most children is formed chiefly from the parent's training and attitudes, through imitation of and identification with the parents. The attitudes and behavior of the parents become impressed on the child's mind and persist in his memory all through life. Because of the very long period of conditioning by his parents, the child introjects his relationship with them and this forms a substantial part of his superego. This becomes a vital and powerful element of his personality both as a child and as an adult. With growth, this superego, this composite of memories and feelings toward his parents is in turn transferred or projected onto others. This projection assumes the form of expectations on the part of the individual that others will react and respond to him much as his parents did.

This does not, however, take only a verbal, conscious form. Its compelling power goes far deeper than that—into the unconscious. There is evidence to suggest that before we learn language our thinking is predominantly accomplished through pictures. We return to this form of visual thinking nightly in our dreams. Apparently the young child forms images in his mind of those persons toward whom he had his first strong feelings. These images are formed as composites, wherein the behavior of each of the key emotional figures is telescoped together. Such *imagoes* comprise and mold the conscience and the person's pattern of attitudes and feelings toward others throughout life. The child who has been reared with love tends to see others as loving; the one who has been brutally treated behaves as though all men were his enemies. If the parents caused guilt in the child, then imagoes will be formed that at once threaten punishment and offer love. And if the training was inconsistent, the result will be conflicting imagoes that cause serious confusion in the mind of the child and later of the adult.

For example, a mother filched from her husband extra allowance money for her son, who knew of this. As an adult he felt he could indulge himself, even illictly, but felt painfully inferior and guilty toward his father and toward other honest, hardworking men. He struggled between indulging himself illegally as his mother had done and being the responsible worker and family man his father was.

It is in the family that the emotional patterns of outlook, feeling, reaction, and behavior (which will form the core of the superego) are shaped. The rest of the personality matures as the body grows, but this core will be affected little in the course of an ordinary life. The conditioning begins at birth and possibly, to some extent, even before that. In general, the younger the organism, the more sensitive it is to emotional influences and the more easily its personality can be damaged. For example, John, whose father had been harsh and dominating from the very beginning, was so sensitized to this treatment that he reacted to everyone who had the least position or even air of authority with a submissive attitude which, inwardly, he could not bear and which enraged him.

His father's image so ruled him that he would even become anxious in the presence of a friendly conductor on the train. As a grown man, John would spend weeks mortally dreading a trip to Europe, which he often had to make for business, because he knew he would have to face the authority of the customs officers. He viewed every superior with suspicion and hostility. It became increasingly difficult for him even to leave his apartment every morning because he knew he would have to pass by the traffic cop on the corner. To give in had once been too painful, too total a yielding of his will; to fight meant identification with those above him, and to his unconscious this meant that he himself would have to become the dictatorial, controlling type of person he despised in his father.

Oddly enough, the overloving parent can create similar threatening imagoes. The superego is often very harsh in persons who were treated, not sternly, but very lovingly during their earliest years. Persons so treated are frequently visited in their dreams by cruel, powerful men and beasts, and their anxiety, however directed, may not leave them by day. Dependent, receptive wishes for love can be made too strong by excessive over-indulgence during childhood. An individual who was raised in this way may feel in his adult relationships that he is toward others too much like the child he was toward his parents. Understandably this gives rise to a general sense of weakness, which in turn generates feelings of envy and rage. But because he has always been lovingly treated, this individual dare not admit to these feelings of hostility. He controls them and is in reality a kind and considerate person. His hostility may be perceived as coming from others (paranoid projection) or it may be acted out against the self (masochism).

Perhaps the best-known fact about social cooperation is that it can arise as an extension of sexual-familial relations. According to Allee: "The more closely knit societies arose from some sort of simple aggregation, frequently . . . of the familial pattern." Sex and family feeling is one expression of the underlying tendency of protoplasm to preserve and expand itself.

Sex involves and is involved in both sensuality and love. Sensuality derives from various bodily erotic zones (for example, lips and mouth, anal region, skin, breasts), which normally contribute to and culminate in genital sensations and orgasm. Thus sex is a physiological mechanism. But it also has a psychological content—love. Actually any strong feeling can be erotized to some degree, and as such, sex can serve the purpose of expressing and draining a variety of feelings. In the mature adult, sex is an expression of love and the mating impulses. In persons who have not matured sufficiently, however, sex, like other biological drives, can be misdirected and misused. For example, it may be used for making money or solely for the purpose of satisfying narcissistic needs for attention and admiration.

Obviously every sexual act, to be mature, need not be for the deliberate and exclusive purpose of procreation; but for maturity, sex must eventually become part of or operate in a setting of love for others. The person who continues to use sex *only* as childish play and as nothing else, who fails to fuse it with love, does not fulfill his adult sexual role in life. The result is usually frustration and pain and guilt, all of which combine to cause hostility. Conversely, if overinhibited or denied all expression, sex can become a major source of anguish and anger.

There are also sources of hostility in sexual feelings themselves. This is true when sex is used as the chief pathway for releasing the body's surplus energy and emotional tensions. For example, one young male patient had such a passion for his girlfriend that he became more and more possessive and jealous. As time went on Fred attempted to attack physically any other boy who made even the most innocent gesture of attention toward his girlfriend. He was only a step away from paranoid jealousy, having already begun to hint at delusions about her unfaithfulness. Fred had been severely deprived emotionally during childhood. His father had been cruel and his mother had merely tolerated him. Thus he grew up with intensified longings for parental love with especial hatred toward his mother for denying him. Subsequently these feelings were transferred to his girlfriend. She meant everything he had desired from a woman throughout childhood and never received, and there also lurked within him, unconsciously, impulses to revenge himself against her as against his depriving mother. The fight-flight reaction was provoked day after day, year after year, by this conflict. Sex meant not love, but selfishness and hate and attack. Led by his mother to see all women as beings who would surely reject him, his sex life was obstructed and, because of this, he burned with hostility that he could not understand or handle. Only by resolving his childhood pattern of internal frustration could he avoid using his relationship to the opposite sex as a means of satisfying his childish needs for love and revenge.

ANXIETY, SEX AND HOSTILITY

In psychiatric usuage, *fear* is used to describe an emotional reaction to a danger that is external and obviously real. For instance, it is reasonable to fear a mad dog if one is near you and growling threateningly. *Anxiety*, however, is a term used to describe feelings of fear that are experienced when no good external reason for them is perceivable, as in the various phobias. Generally speaking, fear is rational while anxiety is not.

However, this distinction breaks down as soon as the reason for the seemingly irrational, neurotic anxiety is understood. The man who fears heights usually does so because, looking down from them, he feels impelled to hurl himself to injury and death. Thus the danger is to him thoroughly real; but it is labeled irrational and unreal because it lies within the man's own motivations, within his often unconscious, self-destructive impulse to jump. The more we probe the reasons for neurotic anxiety, the more we find that there does in fact exist a danger from inner urges that is as real and intelligible as any external threat would be.

What is this inner danger? Studies made of children during wartime bombing raids give some particularly illuminating insights into this question. Anna Freud and Dorothy Burlingham found that small children who felt secure with their parents, and whose parents did not show excessive fear, did not betray signs of fear themselves even in the most threatening of situations. The experimental studies of Liddell, which we mentioned earlier, demonstrate the same principle in animals. You will recall that the twin kid who was separated from its mother broke down under stress while the one that remained with its mother did not.

In contrast to these studies in threatening situations, let us look at the case of the child who is in physically safe circumstances but develops intense neurotic anxiety. Usually such a child is filled with angry impulses, which he is desperately afraid will come out (directly or indirectly). Perhaps they will emerge in the form of forbidden activities and thereby bring down upon him harsh parental punishment. The dreams of children reflect clearly how they struggle with their own forbidden urges to hostile behavior and with their reactions of guilt. Usually in their nightmares, just as in the nightmares of adults, the dangerous animals, witches, bogeymen, and robbers are all representations, or, more accurately, projections of their own destructiveness. They may also be the effects of guilt and consequent tendencies to self-punishment. Guilt stems predominantly, if not exclusively, from hostility, although this may not always be obvious at first glance. Guilt for, say, sexual transgression usually is found to be actually guilt for hurting someone through disloyalty or defiance.

Hostility and fear are very close in the mind. This is in part because of the unconscious mental mechanism of projection, which causes an individual's own inner hostility to appear to come from outside the self. It is then this outside threat that arouses fears. This is clearly seen in delusions of persecution in paranoids. The intimacy of fear and hostility should not be surprising in view of the fact that they have common physiological roots in the fight-flight reaction.

This point is emphasized here because the relationship between these forces is not, as some think, simply a matter of fear causing hostility. It is certainly true that very often fear does arouse hostility—to flee or to destroy the danger. But so, too, time and again, anxieties are found to be produced by hostility. The reality seems to be this: Some frustration, irritation, or even real danger make the child angry, enraged. This hostility is directed against those who rear him, or toward siblings or others in his environment whom he cannot freely vent his anger against. Therefore, because of fear of retaliation or of guilt, love or training, or any combination of these, the hostility must be held in check, controlled, repressed. It is then experienced as anxiety. The patterns thus formed in childhood are then followed, in the main, for life, waxing and waning with the vicissitudes of experience.

The adult's projections of his imagoes and of his reactions to them may distort his concepts not only of individuals, but also of groups, of the social scene, of nations, and of international forces. In fact, it is easier for the unconscious to emerge in relation to large and unfamiliar groups. Contact with actual people who can be seen and spoken with provides the sense of reality that is often sufficient to correct the distortions caused by the imagoes. But nations, for instance, cannot be known in this concrete way, and they tend therefore to be thought of as abstractions. Consequently, they and the leaders who determine their policies are fitted more readily into childhood symbols and imagoes and stereotypes.

Some demagogues and politicians understand this well, although they might express it in other terms. Each person has in his mind something of a bogeyman (either the direct imago of a punishing parent or else a dream creature), which has been formed out of his guilt and his own repressed hostile feelings. Witches and devils and other dangerous creatures of fantasy are usually, as we discussed earlier, projections of the person's own hostility.

There may also be a complementary figure because, let us add, imagoes can be split. Often they are. One male patient loved his very dominating father and in part even enjoyed being under his control because this relieved him of the responsibility of having to make independent decisions. At the same time his masculine pride rebelled and unconsciously he hated the subservience to his father and longed to strike out against him. The patient solved this conflict by always having two men in his life —one whom he could love and another whom he hated.

This so-called splitting of the imago as a solution to the conflict between love and dependence on the one hand and hate on the other, reflects the dualism of a god and a devil. It rests on the fact that it is a very difficult emotional situation for anyone to hate a person whom he also loves and on whom he is dependent. If only that person were two it would be possible to vent both feelings. The origin and appeal of many secular and religious ideologies is that they formulate solutions for just such conflicts. Similarly, demagogues paint pictures that conform to our different imagoes and, by so doing, are able to stir up infantile patterns and direct reservoirs of childhood hostility one way or another with very little regard for reality. In fact, the less reality there is to offer correction, the easier it is to manipulate the imagoes and direct the hostility.

Another aspect of domination by such imagoes is people's own tendency not to face the reality of "personality" in other human beings (to say nothing of animals). This is partly a form of failure of identification, and it underlies all sorts of group prejudices. The individual members of a particular race or group are not seen as human beings like oneself, as having similar strivings and feelings, as loving their mates and children, and as struggling as best they can with the same problems all men face. Instead, the tendency is to amalgamate all the individuals in the group and then apply a label to them, which is typically a fantastic caricature representing the individual's own repressed feelings. Thus a person might try to get rid of his own feelings of inferiority by attributing them to minority groups or to others who are in positions of lesser social or economic status. For example, an individual who loathes his own feelings of deprivation may vent his hatred on the poor, whom he sees as representing these feelings. In similar fashion a person's hostile impulses can be projected onto Wall Street, onto unions, or onto political candidates—just as they were onto witches not so long ago. Projection is a convenient mechanism for it allows the individual to feel: I am good and virtuous—the inferiority, evil, malevolence, hostility is not in me, no, it is there, in him, that is where to seek it and attack it.

How the mechanism of projection operates is seen with great frankness and clarity in dreams. The night before coming for psychiatric treatment one patient dreamed that he opened the door to the basement of his house, saw a big, murderous man below in the darkness, and then slammed the door shut in terror. A woman dreamed that she was chased through an underground tunnel by a man with a knife. Another man, also in reaction to coming for treatment, dreamed that he was exploring underground passages when he came upon an armed intruder whom he attacked and tried to kill in self-defense. Sometimes the malign creature is not a man but a monster or a gang or the representation of some nation or other group, and sometimes the hostility appears as a force of nature, such as a storm, flood, or earthquake, or as a free floating and rather vague terror. Associations showed that in these dreams the cellar and underground passages were symbols of the patient's unconscious, the depths of the mind. There the dreamers saw their own murderous impulses in the threatening figures. The figures, although formed by their own fantasies during sleep, were not recognized by the dreamers as parts of themselves, but appeared to be entirely alien. Hence, there was no conscious sense of identification with them, no empathy or sympathy, and it was therefore possible to release unbridled hostility against them.

It is this same mechanism that makes possible many human brutalities in everyday life. A person sees as alien, feared, and hated those individuals or groups upon whom he projects his own alien, feared impulses. What he cannot face in himself, he sees while asleep in the fantasied figures of his dreams and while awake in those with whom he is not identified. Prejudice is therefore a confession; intolerance announces something intolerable within.

Helen is a young suburban matron who has come to the attention of the psychiatrist because of physical symptoms (recurrent and severe headaches) that she and her regular physician suspect may have an emotional component. Helen is secure in her relationships with her husband and children, and she enjoys considerable financial security as well. She is not aware of feeling prejudice of any sort, and thinks of herself as being entirely

liberal. Despite her conscious thoughts and humanitarian behavior, her dreams clearly reveal, to her utter surpise, unmistakable expressions of racial intolerance.

Helen has a strong tendency to envy and depreciate others.
She becomes extremely tense out of a sense of competition
whenever she is with anyone who can be viewed as an equal or a
superior. Often this evaluation has no basis in reality. For example, she will think that some other woman is better dressed,
or wealthier, or a better tennis player, or more socially acceptable, when in fact none of this may be true. Apparently this pro-
clivity of Helen's is derived largely from feelings of inferiority
and envy toward an older brother. He was clearly favored in the
family all through childhood simply because he was a boy. Coupled with this was the father's persistently negative attitude
toward Helen and his marked lack of parental interest in her.
Thus Helen grew up feeling like an inadequate, unaccepted, and
dominated child. The result is an intense need for acceptance
coupled with virulent competitiveness and envy toward the favored brother.

What a paradox. Here is a woman of uncommon intelligence
with considerable mental and physical attractiveness, wealth,
and social position, and yet she feels herself to be grossly inferior. All her energies are aimed at achieving acceptance. In short,
Helen was born at the top of the social and economic ladder but,
because of the disturbed emotional relationship with her parents, she has the psychology of a social climber.

Her sense of hurt pride along with feelings of rejection, envy,
and frustration supply a chronic source of rage and hostility.
There was never any possibility of expressing these feelings
openly during childhood and so they were strongly inhibited, especially those in regard to her father. He was already so tense
and irritable that any expression of hostility toward him would
surely have exacerbated his negative criticism and rejection of
Helen. All her relationships with people outside the family reflect this childhood pattern and as such persistently generate
feelings of tension and hostility. It is partly for this reason that
she has always felt so much more comfortable with those she
could readily recognize as being inferior to herself. Uncon-

sciously she always tries to get into a position where she can un-
questionably be superior. That is, she manipulates herself into
situations wherein she can assume the parental role. Thus her
recurrent dreams about blacks and Jews and various individuals
of what she sees as lesser social status. Part of Helen's personality feels more comfortable with those she considers social inferiors and this contributes to her being liberal in outlook when it
comes to racial and ethnic minorities. In addition she feels a
certain amount of identification with individuals in these groups
because they represent the underdog to her. This feeling of inferiority was fostered in her childhood and continues as a pattern in her adult life.

Why, then, if Helen prefers being in a superior position and if
she identifies with those she sees as socially inferior does she
harbor these unconscious prejudices? Why isn't this young
woman completely and consistently liberal? The answer is that
Helen also identifies with her parents. She could never, as we
said, rebel against them openly and her repressed hostility generated constant anxiety during childhood. This led her to rather
extreme perfectionism—hoping and striving always to win their
love and attention. Therefore, she could never accept her own
identification with those she saw as inferiors. In fact, Helen
feared and hated ths identification and therefore hated all those
who reminded her of how inferior and inadequate she herself
felt. Further, to identify with the underdog is to feel like one,
and this consists at bottom in feeling like the rejected, guilty,
and inferior child feels toward its parents.

Of course, fearing and wishing to destroy the stranger who is
really the stranger within ourselves is not the only mechanism
operating here. No doubt there is often some element of biological suspiciousness toward the unfamiliar which all animals show
very clearly to some extent. But the mechanism of projection is,
because of early repression, rather specific for human beings
and central in the emotional, irrational roots of prejudice. Its
fateful significance, moreover, lies in its distortion of reality to
fit the emotional needs and in its impairment of the adult capacity for cooperation, which is the very foundation of the human family and society and of human security.

External factors may also produce hostility, although it is

doubtful whether they are ever a basic source. Even in those societies where anger and hate are encouraged as a social characteristic, early training must be given in order to insure the successful inculcation of these qualities. For instance, anthropologist Margaret Mead constrasts the Arapesh of New Guinea with the Mundugumor. The latter are violent, hateful, and cannibalistic; while among the former such hostile behavior is rare and regarded as pathological. Dr. Mead ascribes some of the differences between these cultural groups to the way each one raises its children. The Arapesh are kind to theirs, and responsibility for all the young members of the tribe is shared by several individual families. Each child, therefore, is brought up to believe that he has many parents besides his own. If he has trouble with his real father, mother, or siblings, he has a whole series of substitutes to turn to. Through conditioning, the intense emotional relationships characteristically found in the immediate family are diluted and he learns from infancy on to feel secure with many people. The Mundugumor, on the other hand, treat the child from birth in a manner guaranteed to arouse his rage. For example, the infant is typically pulled half-suckled from the breast, and the behavior of his parents and other adults encourages him to vent his angers freely in action.

Closer to home we often see how frustrations engendered by poor housing and education, by illness and poverty, tend to brutalize human beings. Clearly it is urgent to find solutions to these problems; but it must at the same time be noted that history has not shown that brutality and hostility are reactions to material circumstance alone. Great leaders and despots alike have come from shacks as well as palaces, slums as well as well-groomed suburbs. Semistarvation, chronic disease, or relative well-being provide only one factor in shaping personality. Emotional reactions to people in adult life continue and repeat the emotional reactions to people that were formed in the earliest years of childhood. Indubitably it is the emotional relations of the earliest years, these conditioning interpersonal relations, that are the great, predominant factor in the development of the hostile mind. External factors serve to bring out the hostility by putting pressure upon those patterns already made vulnerable by the experiences of childhood.

Part Three

HOSTILODYNAMIC MECHANISMS

They went forth to battle, but they always fell;
. . . .
Nobly they fought and bravely, but not well,
. . . .
It was a secret music that they heard,
   A sad sweet plea for pity and for peace. . . .

SHAEMAS O'SHEEL

Chapter 6

HOSTILITY AND PERSONALITY

The history of man's hostility begins with man's history. As Willem Van Loon pointed out in *The Arts*, the subject of the earliest known picture drawn by prehistoric man is that of men killing one another. In the very first chapter of the Bible we find murder: "And Cain talked with Abel his brother; and it came to pass when they were in the field that Cain rose up against Abel and slew him." Parallel with these kinds of individual acts of violence, or possible in defense against them, the bonds of society developed. Then religion, law, and morality developed, but this did not put an end to violence. Indeed, if anything, man's coming together in communities extended his destructiveness for now entire tribes and city-states could attack each other. The individual was no longer restricted to one-to-one combat. Today nations and teams of nations fight counterparts of differing political, economic, and social ideologies, and perhaps at some time in the future interplanetary war will be possible.

Hostility persists and in fact is supported on a grand scale, but there has been a notable change in moral emphasis, in how the human personality handles this destructive potential. The feeling that wars will get you something (food, shelter, land, glory) has shifted to a feeling that wars will only help you to defend something (home, family, country, and way of life). At least today excuses must be advanced for warring—a nation can no longer go to war frankly and exclusively for fun and gain. Is it then unreasonable to hope that if excessive hostility can be recognized as an adaptive mechanism that is as vestigial and useless as the appendix, progress toward peaceful cooperation will be hastened?

The place to uproot hostility is at the source of its transmission—from within the family pattern. But to accomplish this, the dynamics of hostility must be isolated, studied, and understood. The expression of hostility by the adult personality is determined not only by the intensity of the feeling but also by the ways in which it is handled.

In the technical language of psychiatry, the hostility, arising in various forms, intensities, and in combination with other motivations from the id (the biological source of impulses), is handled by the superego (the conscience with its nucleus of biosocial cooperativeness plus early, and to some extent later, conditioning) and by the ego (the intellect, reason, the conscious faculties). The ego and superego can permit or they can control and transform. To do the latter, that is, to defend an individual from unrestrained acting out of impulses, mechanisms of defense are used. (Technically these can be distinguished from mechanisms of conscious control, but for our purposes we need not separate them.) We pass then from a consideration of the sources and characteristics of hostility to an examination of its status relative to the rest of the personality.

The many and varied manifestations of hostility can be grouped to fit into three major categories. This grouping depends mostly upon how freely the individual, in his ego and in his conscience, can consciously and unconsciously accept and act out his hostile impulses. Hence the categories are organized to describe behavior ranging from full criminality, through varying degrees and forms of repression, to transformations of the destructive hostility into socially constructive activity. In other words, the groups reflect behavior ranging from direct and open hostile actions against other individuals and against society, through more or less inhibited, disguised hostility to other individuals, to actual social constructiveness. We will identify these groups as (1) antisocial, (2) private, (3) social.

Antisocial behavior toward other individuals and society is a broad category covering three principal mechanisms for handling hostility: the criminal, the criminoid, and the neurotic criminal. The criminal mechanism is characterized by the fact that the hostility is accepted by the person, in his ego and conscience, and is deliberately acted out in antisocial form. The criminoid mechanism is characterized by the fact that the hostility is not fully accepted by the person, who defends himself against acting it out directly in antisocial form but who is willing to act it out indirectly, usually within the confines of the law. The neurotic criminal mechanism is characterized by the fact that although the person indulges in direct antisocial behavior, he does not fully accept it and punishes himself for it in various ways.

The second category includes what we may call the private ways of handling hostility. The basic mechanisms in this category are: the neurotic character, the classic neurosis, and psychosomatic disorder. The mechanism of the neurotic character is distinguished by the fact that the hostility, inadequately repressed, may not be antisocially directed but may cause instead suffering only to the individual himself and to those involved with him personally. An example of this would be the self-destructiveness observed in alcoholics and compulsive gamblers. The mechanism of the classic neurosis is characterized by the fact that the hostility, repressed successfully in behavior, produces specific symptoms for the sufferer (such as anxiety, phobias, hysterical mood swings) and also makes life miserable for his intimates. The psychosomatic mechanism is characterized by the complete absence of a direct expression of the hostility toward others. The person who remains calm and gentle while seething inside would be a typical example. The hostility affects only himself by, for example, manifesting itself as headaches, stomach or bowel disorders, or elevated blood pressure.

The third category of behavior describes the social handling of hostility. The fundamental mechanism involved here is that of sublimation, which is characterized by the fact that the hostility is used constructively for the welfare of individuals and society.

These dynamics, as seen in clinical practice, are summarized in the chart on the following page. It shows the three major categories and the seven principal dynamic mechanisms involved in handling hostility. The term and category *criminoid* are new but their usefulness will become clear in the next chapter, where they are discussed in detail. The first four groups, from left to right, reflect an attempt to separate the types of persons usually lumped together under the wastebasket label of "psychopathic personality." This very broad term can be misleading and ambiguous since it may range from an innocuous eccentric to a brutal murderer.

The heading under which an individual is placed depends on how intensively and predominantly one or more of these mechanisms operates in his emotional make-up and behavior. Such differentiations are deep-going because of the fundamental importance of hostility in all psychopathology, in all personalities, and in everyday human affairs. Hostility occupies a place in psychological processes that is quite analogous to that of heat in physical processes. All mechanical friction generates heat. All emotional friction generates hostility. Hence, just as thermodynamics is a fundamental branch of physics, so the dynamics of hostility is a fundamental branch of psychiatry and can properly be called *hostilodynamics.*

How the hostility is handled, that is, the extent to which each of the above mechanisms is used in the personality, depends upon the intensity of the hostility and upon the maturity and health of the ego and the superego. If the hostility grossly distorts the sense of reality and behavior, but if the person nevertheless remains adequately responsible for himself and others, the result is a psychotic character. If, as in more extreme cases, the processes of reason are so excessively distorted that the person is incapable of taking care of himself, then the result is psy-

HOSTILODYNAMIC MECHANISMS Form, direction and status of hostilities as seen in clinical categores. All of these dynamics probably exist in some degree and proportion in everyone, always mixed with others. They may be: (1) latent, (2) reactive, (3) character traits, regular or occasional.

HOSTILITY EXPRESSED	ANTISOCIAL — TOWARD OTHER INDIVIDUALS AND SOCIETY			PRIVATE — TOWARD OTHER INDIVIDUALS BUT NOT AGAINST SOCIETY		PRIVATE — WITHIN SELF	SOCIAL — USED CONSTRUCTIVELY TOWARD OTHERS AND SOCIETY
	CRIMINAL	CRIMINOID	NEUROTIC CRIMINAL	NEUROTIC CHARACTER	CLASSIC NEUROSIS	PSYCHO-SOMATIC DISORDER	SUBLIMATION
	Hostility is accepted and deliberately acted out in antisocial form.	Hostility is defended against in direct, antisocial form but acted out indirectly and within the law.	Hostility is acted out in direct antisocial form but defenses cause self-induced suffering.	Hostility, defended against and repressed, is acted out in indirect, distorted form toward other individuals (but not antisocially) and with self-induced suffering.	Hostility, defended against and repressed, generates neurotic symptoms, indirectly affecting other individuals but not in an antisocial way.	Hostility, defended against and generally repressed, produces physical symptoms, not acted out directly or indirectly against other individuals or society.	Hostility, direct or transformed, is used for welfare of others and society.

Left margin (range indicators):

NEUROTIC — Range, levels ←→

PSYCHOTIC — Range, levels ←→

PSYCHOTIC EQUIVALENTS

EGO ←→

Sound, reality-sense, integration, and control. ←→ Marked distortion by emotional forces of reality-sense, integration, and control.

Right margin (directional scales):

More toward others, antisocial ←——→ Less toward others, more social — *Hostility Directed*

Less mature, social, effective ←——→ More mature, social, effective — *Superego*

Accepts hostile impulses, behavior ←——→ Rejects hostile impulses, behavior — *Ego* chosis. But insofar as psychosis is only an extreme form of neurosis, it reveals no basically new mechanisms for the handling of hostility. The fundamental feature is the relative weakness of the ego in coping with motivations from id and superego, so that the person's feelings can distort his ego functioning, including his thinking and sense of reality, and even lead to frank delusions and hallucinations, or to total disruption of reason. Extremely psychotic persons are, just because of this, usually easy to recognize. However, in the milder cases the person may exercise considerable influence in society without being recognized as psychotic. Many individuals distort only that portion of reality that serves directly the purposes of their hostility.

Of course, no one individual handles all of his hostilities exclusively in the manner described for each category. These seem like sharp divisions, whereas, in reality people regularly show mixtures of these mechanisms in their behavior. If a large series of actual cases were arranged in order, they would form a continuous spectrum, a gradation from one extreme to the other. Nevertheless, just as separate colors can be perceived as such in the solar spectrum even though the whole is a continuum, so these major categories can be differentiated by the predominance of one or another mechanism for handling the hostility.

In discussing any of these mechanisms a very important factor must be identified, that is, the extent to which the motivation is internal or reactive. A quite social person who is by no means given to criminal acts, can generate such rage under certain external conditions that he loses control of himself, bypasses his judgment and standards, and commits acts that are seemingly out of character. Examples of this would be what are commonly called "crimes of passion." Under sufficient external pressure, especially if it bears on his particular emotional vulnerabilities, the most stable individual can break down (or break out) into hostile behavior. On the other hand, many persons in satisfactory life circumstances indulge, without any apparent external provocation, in cruel behavior out of internal motivations. Thus in every category the hostility and the way it is handled, that is, the hostilodynamic mechanism, may appear as latent, as reactive to unusual external stress, or as a character trait (emerging occasionally or regularly).

Another feature is of great importance. External or emotional pressures can alter the intensity of an individual's hostility and the way in which he handles it. Therefore it is possible for a person to shift, temporarily at least, from one mechanism to another. But how easily the latent hostility can be aroused in him and how far he will go depends chiefly upon his basic character patterns. Under the influence of physical or emotional hardships or temptations, or under the sway of demagoguery, there is an increasing chance that the conscience will be lulled or bribed, or that the grasp of reality will weaken and hostility break through, or that neuroses or psychoses will develop.

Our chief concern will not be with these mechanisms as evoked by traumatic external events and acted out in brief, transient episodes. Rather our attention will be directed more to persons who show them as part of an accustomed way of life, as a permanent character trait.

The distinction between private and antisocial hostility reflects a contrast that is frequently observed in everyday experience. Many people treat their own families very differently from the way they treat other individuals, other groups, and society at large. A man may be a criminal killer and involved in all sorts of illegalities and still be kind to his wife and children. Conversely, another man may be a constructive figure in his occupation and in the community and yet be a tyrant on the domestic scene.

We can see this same thing very plainly on the psychotic level, where the tendency to regress to childhood patterns is strong enough to derange the perceptive, integrative, and executive functions of the ego. As noted earlier, in some of the milder forms of psychosis the individual may even manage to get by quite well in society. History records many examples of such psychotic individuals. Because they were plausible enough in most areas, they were able to become fringe political leaders. By their very intensity and extremism they could arouse emotional resonance in others. In magnified form, these men expressed personality tendencies that were latent in their followers.

The same hate, rage, and impulse to attack may come out in the criminal in direct murder. In the depressed patient it may manifest itself in overwhelming self-reproach or even suicide.

And psychosomatically it may find expression in an epileptic attack or some other severe illness.

It may even show up disguised as pleasure. This exercise of a function for pleasure rather than for survival is called *erotization*. Franz Alexander, in his *Fundamentals of Psychoanalysis*, sees it as an expression of surplus energy not needed by the organism for growth, propagation, or maintaining a livelihood. Muscular powers are used for enjoyment in sport. People eat because they like it as well as for calories. Similarly, some people fight, or create fights, because they enjoy them. This is seen in varying degrees throughout history. In the Roman circuses condemned men and women were turned loose among wild beasts to be torn to pieces for the pleasure of the audience. Among some tribes of American Indians, fighting was frankly a form of play and as such a source of great enjoyment. Even today, war is not wholly a means to an end. Furthermore, little children play war for fun; adults relish the brutality of boxing and prize fighting; and dramas of violence and brutality today often become instant box-office successes because of the enormous following that violence attracts.

There is a tendency for any strong emotion to be connected with sexual feelings, that is, to become erotized. All during life every person has sex hormones circulating in his bloodstream and, especially during maturity, is under constant sexual pressure. This pressure is reflected subjectively in the mind, which fills with sexual impulses and fantasies that are more or less repressed, disguised, or elaborated. A prime function of the mind is integration. It naturally integrates the sex drives and feelings with other motivating forces. Because of the pervasiveness of the sexual feelings, they can easily mix with hostility.

Surely one of the most sinister features of hostility is this ready fusion with sexual feelings. Hostility can be aroused by sexual feelings and it can arouse sexual feelings. Sadism, which is far more widespread than is recognized, means pleasure, including full sexual responses, derived through inflicting cruelty. There are people who reach orgasm only by causing pain to another. Here sex expresses hate and violence, not love. Such persons can enjoy sexual satisfaction through every form of brutality.

Sexual pleasure in pillage, violence, cruelty, and killing has written many pages of history. Man has gotten sexual pleasure from the worst tortures he can fantasy. Caillou observes: "The tiger will kill only when he's hungry, and the lion only when he's disturbed. The elephant won't harm you unless you're fool enough to go between him and his females, and even the crocodile will let you swim if his larder is full. But the leopard . . . for the sheer enjoyment of killing, just for the pleasure of it . . . kills because he likes it. There's only one other animal that does that . . . and that's man." As Gregory Zilboorg noted in his *Psychology of Criminal Acts*, some murderers experience multiple orgasms during the deed. So did some soldiers when shooting an enemy or when in extreme danger of being shot themselves. Certain persons get their sexual satisfaction out of being threatened, beaten, or otherwise badly treated. In this sexual masochism, the need to be punished is erotized and becomes an essential component of gratification.

Before proceeding to a detailed look at each of the dynamic mechanisms for handling hostility, let us summarize the variables involved: (1) the early conditioning, which by stimulating hostility determines its intensity in the id; (2) the proportional strengths of the disordered infantile patterns and the mature motivations; (3) the different forces that keep the hostility going, such as frustrated infantile demands for love or prestige; (4) the direction and degree of fixation of the hostility on certain imagoes and its transferability to other persons; (5) the degree to which the hostility is accepted in its different forms and directions by the superego; (6) whether the superego operates in advance or with constant effectiveness or whether it permits acting out and then brings down punishment; and (7) the extent to which the conscious ego accepts the restrictions of the superego or to which it feels justified in accepting the hostility with or without later punishment. All this will be made concrete and more readily comprehensible in the following chapters through discussion and examples of each of the categories.

Chapter 7

ANTISOCIAL MECHANISMS

The literature devoted to the genetic-dynamic sources of criminality is relatively meager, though now rapidly expanding. The older theories that criminality is congenital and hereditary can be given little credence since the facts offered in support of such theories are totally inadequate. And while it is certainly conceivable that physical, developmental defects in the brain itself may result in uncontrolled criminal behavior, these cases are not the ones that concern us here, and any theory as to congenital or hereditary factors producing such functional effects in the intact organism still carries the burden of proving itself.

We are safe, then, in assuming that, according to present knowledge, the child who develops into a criminal character either has been subjected to gross mistreatment during his early years or he has been provided with a model for this kind of behavior by one or both parents or by others to whom he was emotionally attached. Without this background, even strong influences toward criminality usually fail. For instance, in so-called high crime areas the accepted social standard among a child's playmates frequently involves direct participation in juvenile gangsterism. If a child does not accept this neighborhood ideology and join in with the gang, he not only may be ostracized and despised, but his actual physical safety may be threatened. Nevertheless, not every child in such a crime area becomes a delinquent and later a criminal. If the family influence on the child has been stable and healthy enough, despite all group pressures and threats of retaliation, he will not accept criminal patterns of behavior or, even if he does so at the time, he soon outgrows them. So, too, in later life, a man or woman under great external pressure and in spite of every temptation may never behave in a criminal fashion because this is too foreign to his personality. The twig must have been bent in childhood in the direction of crime for the tree to be so inclined.

We call *criminal* the kind of person whose makeup is such that he accepts, as part of his accustomed behavior, his hostile feelings against other human beings and is willing deliberately to act out these feelings. He may injure other people through crimes against their property, such as theft, or through crimes against their person, such as assault. The career criminal may show no impairment in his sense of reality or intelligence, but the mature restraints of identification, empathy, social feeling, and a normal conscience do not seriously hamper his overt hostile behavior.

Throughout our discussion we treat crime in the sense of injury to life and the living, particularly human life and human living. By injury we mean not only bodily damage, mild or severe, but anything that impairs development and adjustment, individual liberty, and happiness. An injury is thus considered criminal if widespread perpetration of it would threaten the foundations and functions of society. It should be noted that this definition is basically independent of any laws or customs that may or may not exist in a particular community. In fact, if the laws injure human life and living, then the laws themselves may be termed criminal. This would hold true in our mind even for a savage community like the Mundugumor, mentioned previously, wherein the mores are described as involving free acceptance of a relatively large amount of hostility in violent behavior. In this society the noncriminal citizen is the exception and the eccentric.

Of course not every inconvenience that someone imposes upon us need be called a crime; essentially we are seeking for the quality, which can be isolated and properly described as criminal. This quality seems to be an inner, psychological one, a mechanism that conceivably can and perhaps does exist to a quantitatively different extent in everyone. Its essence is an individual's acceptance in his ego of sufficient hostility for him to act it out with relative freedom against other human beings for selfish personal purposes.

An analogy with illness may clarify the use of the term *quality*. If a person has a sniffle, he is not considered by himself or others to be sick. If he has a tiny splinter in his finger, he does not call it an injury. But while these are mild, perhaps even negligible conditions, still their essential quality is harm to the organism. In like manner you would not label a relatively minor offense, such as maliciously slighting a person's name or trampling a neighbor's lawn, a crime. Nevertheless, such an act, however negligible in quantity, may in its quality be criminal.

This formula naturally must be used with caution. Human behavior is difficult to judge. Usually it is essential to know the motives. Suppose a person injures, even kills, another for purposes of self-defense. If the main motivation is mature, and life-preservative for himself, his family, or country, if the act is not done out of egoistic malevolence, then it lacks the essential quality of criminality. The purpose of an act may even be constructive though the means used may take a hostile form. For instance, the policeman who shoots a killer solely to defend society and its members is not acting criminally; but, on the other hand, if he commits the same act out of personal motives, such as thrill, revenge, or self-aggrandizement, then psychologically the act itself is criminal despite its socially good results. Because of the rampant immaturity in the world, peace must often be maintained through force, and, unfortunately, only too frequently men use the authority of law as a mask for their own criminal mechanisms. Criminality is also seen in different form among individuals who commit crimes more for emotional satisfaction than for material gain and economic security.

Thus to understand the hostilodynamic mechanism in a given person and circumstance, not only the act itself, but its external purpose in the mind of the doer as well as his internal feelings in the doing of it must be considered, for crime is basically motivational, psychological. This distinction is seen repeatedly in fiction. The hero presumably kills "more in sorrow than in anger." And he is able to do so only because he feels that it is for some worthy, necessary purpose, such as protecting the heroine or defending his honor or country. The villain, however, freely accepts cruelty as a means to achieve selfish ends. Often, in fact, he is portrayed as deriving his chief satisfactions from the evil act itself. Happily for human welfare, the majority of people do not find such hostile impulses acceptable to their consciences or their conscious judgment. Society rests on the capacity of individuals to control and sublimate hostility. Therefore, no society is or can ever be entirely safe, secure, and stable.

Everyone has been in situations where, impelled by anger, he has nevertheless not felt free to satisfy his hostile impulse and has restrained himself. This is *suppression*, or conscious control, which is exerted by the ego. Many of us, too, have been trained from infancy to restrain or even reject such impulses entirely. These then become unthinkable and are checked before they can even reach consciousness. Such automatic, unconscious *repression* is powered by the superego rather than by the ego. Impulses thus blocked from direct expression may seek other paths and may produce neurotic, psychotic, or psychosomatic symptoms instead of criminal behavior. More about these later.

Before looking at two criminal case histories, certain points must be made clear. It was perhaps Freud's main discovery that most of what goes on in our minds is remote from awareness. Most feelings, reactions, and thoughts are not conscious. Any form of analytic, psychodynamic therapy depends as a first step upon insight, upon making conscious the major elements of the interplay of motivations, reactions, and feelings. This is accomplished by a somewhat laborious process of fitting together childhood pattern, personal history, and pattern of present life with the patterns of free association and the interpretation of dreams and of earliest memories. Most of this information must come from the patient himself, for the same forces that keep the main dynamics unconscious (shame, guilt, anxiety, and the like) naturally resist attempts to make them conscious. Therefore, this can only be accomplished in persons with relatively strong therapeutic urges, that is, in individuals who are strongly motivated to reveal themselves because of sincere wishes to relieve their psychic suffering. It is these persons who come for help to the private practitioner. Usually these people have considerable maturity and intelligence; they are well motivated to reopen their emotional development and are usually delighted with the insights gained into themselves.

Antisocial persons usually do not have any such wholesome therapeutic urge. They do not come voluntarily for help. Like Mary, the subject of our first vignette, they are already in the throes of the legal system and are ordered by the court, however sympathetically, to have an interview with a doctor whose specialty they do not understand. The psychiatrist is typically seen as an authority to whom it is unsafe to reveal anything about oneself. Therefore it is difficult or impossible to elicit, in the time available, the first memories, free associations, dreams with associations—that is, all the paths to the dynamics we want to understand. This limits the vividness of the following vignettes. We are able to present enough analytic material to see that there has been gross abuse in early childhood and that this is causal for the current dynamics; but we are unable to present enough of the unconscious emotional data to convey a sufficiently deep feeling to the reader. The good analyst, as Freud said, "Feels his way into the patient's emotional life." But that takes time and much desire on the patient's part; both of which are lacking in these persons seen only a few times and only at the behest of the courts, not of the individuals.

In private practice the goal for effective therapy is to understand, in detail, using all the tools we have mentioned (first memories, dreams, history, life pattern, and so on), the patient's childhood emotional pattern of interaction with those close to it and responsible for it, especially from conception to age six. We also want to see, in detail, how extensively and intensively this childhood pattern is affecting the patient's present-day life. It is the operation in the adult of this childhood emotional pattern that is, as we have said in earlier chapters, the basic cause of psychosomatic, neurotic, and psychotic symptoms, and of acting out against oneself and others, that is, the basic cause of all psychopathology.

In the vignettes we can indicate this, but not demonstrate it in full detail. We tried to obtain clear convincing cases from the F.B.I. and the courts, but found very little interest on the part of our justice system in the basic causes of antisocial behavior. Nevertheless, we have seen and read enough that fits perfectly with the experience with private patients to state with confidence that patterns of antisocial behavior, as of all psychopathology, are formed by abuse in the rearing of children. This is as certain as the laws of gravity, but if you are cautious, consider it as a theory to be tested, but realize that it is the most important theory for humanity in the world today.

Let us now look at our two criminal case histories, which reveal some of the key dynamic mechanisms involved in criminality.

Mary, a teenager from a depressed urban area, is presently being kept at a center for delinquent girls as the result of her involvement with a gang of girls in the murder of another teenager. It is thought that Mary is the one member of the gang who is actually responsible for the stabbing that occurred. Mary's story is that she and several friends were walking down the street after a dance when they met the victim, who was with a male companion and another girl. Someone in the gang bet the victim that she could not beat up Mary. The group then egged the two girls on, but Mary claims that she tried, unsuccessfully, to walk away several times. Finally she agreed to fight the victim, and in the ensuing scuffle managed to pull the other girl's coat over her head. Mary says that she then felt something wet and realized that it was blood. Mary denies having stabbed the victim.

Mary's family consists of her mother and an older brother, Lester. The children's father, whose whereabouts are unknown, never played any role in their lives and was never married to their mother. He was, by all available reports, an irresponsible and sadistic individual. Mary's mother, like her daughter, was also illegitimate. During the woman's childhood she was subjected to consistently extreme violence, being savagely beaten and abused regularly. Her mother (Mary's grandmother) was finally put in prison for child abuse. Mary's brother, who is now in jail serving time for armed robbery and aggravated assault, was an overactive and wild child. Mary's mother was determined not to have another child like this. So from the time of her daughter's birth, the woman says she was very controlling and protective toward Mary. She constantly checked up on her to make sure she was not doing anything wrong, and she repeatedly warned Mary about an endless variety of things that might conceivably go awry.

Mary's earliest memory is of standing in her crib all alone at night crying. No one came to attend to her although her mother and she lived in the same room. At first Mary reacted to her mother by being quiet and obedient and by preferring to be alone. She would play with pots and pans or the one doll that she had for hours on end. After a while, when she was three or four years old, her mother tried to get her to play with other young children, but Mary seemed disinterested or perhaps she simply did not know how to play and socialize. She had really had no experience as a toddler in developing the required skills and feelings. Consequently, she daydreamed a lot and would say very little. Mary's lack of responsiveness made her mother angry but the woman did not know how to punish her daughter except to berate her. Since the woman had been so brutally treated as a child herself, she vowed "never to lay a hand on Mary. No matter what!" But her anger at the child did show through; whether or not she did in fact lay a hand on her we do not know.

When it came time for Mary to attend kindergarten she refused to go. Her mother then started a pattern that was to last to the present, that is, she bribed her daughter into going. Although they were on relief and thus had severely limited financial resources, the mother sacrificed spending anything on herself and Lester and instead bought things for Mary. A pretty new dress got her into kindergarten. Mary received toys, clothes, candy, and the like almost on demand while her mother and brother were literally in rags and often in a state of rage.

In her early school years Mary made a quiet and marginal adjustment. She did average work but had great difficulty relating to her peers and was increasingly excluded by them. Most of her teachers felt sorry for this neat, clean, sad little girl who seemed so out of step with the other children. Mary gradually developed a stubborness at school that prevented her from trying anything new or doing anything she was not particularly eager to do. Bribes and promises were the only way teachers could break through her resistance. When Mary would complain to her mother about anything going wrong at school, her mother would reassure the girl by always blaming the teacher or the other children. She frequently told Mary that they would soon be moving out of their neighborhood into a better one where people would act nicer to her. Since her mother made a show of protectiveness toward Mary, as did her teachers to some extent, the children frequently teased her and called her deprecating names. When Mary felt this was getting too upsetting, her mother would keep her out of school for a few days.

By the time she was in fourth grade, Mary became slightly more outgoing and went through the initial stages of developing a few friendships with peers. However, her mother was highly critical of the children Mary chose and did not allow her daughter to see them outside of school. Mary gradually developed a double life, whereby she would see whomever she wanted to and not disclose it to her mother. By the sixth grade she was openly lying to her mother about where she went and with whom. By the seventh grade Mary's behavior at school began to deteriorate rapidly. This heretofore quiet, stubborn, and uninvolved youngster became defiant and rude to her teachers, using profanity and threats of violence. She terrorized and physically beat up younger children so they would turn over their lunch money to her. Before long she developed her own gang to aid her in this. Her mother was called to school repeatedly, but usually she denied the possibility of Mary's misbehaving. Typically she would blame the teachers or other students for picking on her daughter, whom she saw as a quiet, innocent, persecuted, and misunderstood little girl. One day at school Mary shattered the angelic image that her mother struggled to maintain when she viciously attacked an elderly teacher who was reprimanding her. So many students witnessed this attack and testified against Mary that her mother was forced to recognize that her daughter had serious behavior problems.

Mary was suspended and assigned to a special school for disciplinary problems. Her mother became irritated both at the school system and at Mary, whom she started punishing by not allowing her out after school or during the weekend. Mary was not about to be made a prisoner. She countered her mother's punitive measures by sneaking out of the second floor window. She joined a street gang that fought other gangs, shoplifted, snatched purses, and mugged elderly people. Mary was speedy of foot and clever enough not to be arrested in these gang activities until the fight in which she allegedly stabbed another girl to death.

For all her hostility, Mary seems timid and fearful of her environment and expresses concern over abandonment and her own self-image. She feels isolated and afraid of the power of others. The world, to her, is basically hostile, following her early pattern toward her mother and brother. She is highly dependent on her mother, and is unable to express her feelings freely, suppressing much of her hostility because of this dependency. In the past this hostility had been channeled through gang activities. Mary has expressed the feeling that in many ways her mother was not a real mother to her or she would treat her better. Mary gives the very distinct impression that she is trying to deny that her mother was often enraged at her and that she was often beaten by the woman.

Regarding the murder for which she is being retained in custody, Mary feels no sorrow or remorse. She hated the deceased girl, who was known by her peers to be sneaky and deceitful. Mary had a particular loathing for the victim because the latter was much more successful than Mary in leading a double life, that is, in presenting an innocent facade while at the same time stealing, using drugs, and being excessively promiscuous. Mary was jealous of this girl and detested her for having succeeded where she failed.

This case shows clearly some of the limitations we discussed in our note preceding this vignette. It is rare to see violence and murder in an individual if there has been no violence whatever in childhood. We know Mary was very hostile to her mother, but the reasons for it are not clear. We have no definite information on how her mother, who had herself been so brutally treated in childhood, actually felt and behaved toward her daughter. There must have been something in her mother's feelings and behavior to which Mary reacted with such hostility, and probably some example of violence that Mary followed in the stabbing. Mary and her mother frequently offer unsolicited denials of any physical violence in their relationship, but we remain skeptical. Most of the pattern would fall into place if her mother, though she vowed not to, did in fact lose control and strike or even beat the child. But we lack evidence from Mary's dreams, memories, or associations or from outside sources to support this or to disprove it.

The second case history is for some reasons even more intriguing than the vignette about Mary. Primarily this is true because George was not the kind of person in whom you would expect to find the criminal mechanism flourishing. Nevertheless, from a psychological point of view, this man was a killer.

George was a high-powered business executive, smooth and charming in appearance and manner, and very successful in public life. Privately, however, he was coldly hostile to his wife while at the same time professing to be madly in love and full of admiration for her. In his office he was calm in exterior; at home he was usually very agitated and sometimes violent. More than once he had deliberately destroyed expensive possessions that his wife valued. George sought psychiatric treatment because he found himself methodically planning to kill his wife.

The background for his distortion of personality was traceable, as always, to specific warping influences during childhood.

His father had been much preoccupied with his own affairs and remote emotionally from the mother and children except for one daughter toward whom he showed great favoritism. George's mother was an unstable woman of violent temper and hates. She was free with family beatings and on one occasion inflicted rather serious injury upon one of the children in the neighborhood. It is not known whether or not she fought with the father physically, for when George was not yet six his mother left home, abandoning the family. The father remarried soon thereafter; his second marriage was also of short duration.

George was not conscious of any hostility against his father or his preferred younger sister. All of his conscious hostility was turned against the imago of his mother, though he had no concrete conscious memory of her. He could not recall what she looked like, how she acted or dressed, or even any specific incident about her. What remained in his mind was the imago of a person whom he blamed for all the unhappiness and frustration of his childhood. Whether or not the father directly encouraged this feeling is unclear; what is known is that this picture of his mother became the object of his every resentment. He grew up with very few friends, continuing toward other persons the emotional remoteness that he experienced from his father and took over himself as a defense.

The only person with whom he had any sort of warm, emotional relationship was his younger sister, whom he both loved and envied. No one can develop properly nor can most people even continue to live without having at least one reasonably good human relationship. In all probability, this affection for his sister saved George from severe mental disorder. It became the model for what friendly rapport he was able to manage in his adult life. Patterns of kindliness, which this relationship contained, repeated themselves toward his children and served to protect them from his otherwise nearly irresistible hostile impulses.

What in his wife's emotional make-up led her to marry him need not concern us here beyond her appreciation of his fine surface qualities plus identification with him and a masochistic attraction to danger, which grew out of her own disturbed childhood. His feelings toward her repeated at first the profound longing for a good mother, which he had felt during the earliest years of his life. But, of course, as an adult this longing was far too primitive and infantile. It was not the need to love and be loved, which is appropriate in maturity; rather his feelings contained all the intensity of the small child's demands upon its mother. As such, they were foredoomed to frustration. Thwarted in his needs, he soon felt toward his wife the same disappointment he had felt as a child toward his mother—along with a similarly implacable rage. And his mother, with her beatings, provided the model for venting hostility through actual physical violence.

Meanwhile, a neurotic mechanism of hostility also showed in his overanxiety about his children. On rare occasions he might lose control and strike one, but then would soon feel guilt and remorse. Though jealous and resentful of them at times, following the pattern toward his younger sister, he could not, without inner conflict, take out his hostilities upon them. He repressed these feelings, but under their pressure he developed a sense of anxiety about the children. Neurotically he felt that they were in danger, but because he did not realize that the danger lay in his own motivations, his own hostilities, he was constantly overly protective toward them. (Insufficient material was available to demonstrate specifically the source of this pattern of defense and protectiveness.)

By contrast, the hostility toward his wife became conscious. This his ego and superego permitted. Having unconsciously placed his wife in the role of his mother, he now felt free to revenge himself upon her for his mother's beatings and the desertion of him as a child. George planned his wife's murder precisely and repeatedly, never aware that this was following his pattern of feelings toward his mother in childhood. This acceptance of hostility and the willingness to act upon it is unmistakably the criminal mechanism; it convicts him psychologically. Although his wife died a natural death and he never carried out his designs against her, this man was psychologically, in his intent, a criminal in that he had murderous impulses that his ego and superego would, apparently, have permitted him to act out.

One added word about this case. George's infantile impulses did not discriminate between his mother and his wife. This failure is probably much more common in criminals than is generally believed and explains those superficially bewildering incidents that appear from time to time in the newspapers. A vivid example of this was the recent case of two men in their early twenties who assaulted and beat to death a harmless, middle-aged man whom they had never seen before and who was not even worth robbing. The status and intensity of the hostility in these two young men, regardless of who or what shaped it during their formative years, was now such that it could be taken out on almost anyone, even on a complete stranger. This "displacement" is a basic characteristic of hostility; there is a spread to other persons, to animals, or even to inanimate objects of the child's revengeful hatred of his original offenders.

Ugly and antihuman as is the frank criminal, there is another type of personality that can be equally, if not more, sinister: the criminoid. This type complements the criminal and makes organized crime possible. Criminoid behavior is so widespread that we might consider it a characteristic of our times. Although this type of person stays within the letter of the law, his way of living, his decisions, his social and political attitudes reflect his hostility to mankind and his subtle destructiveness to society and its cooperative goals.

The overt criminal is relatively direct and honest about his antisocial hostility. But the criminoid, in contrast, does nothing openly for which he could be charged in the courts. His hostility, although acted out, is masked and disguised as legal and proper. Indeed, he may appear to himself and to a great part of the community as a model citizen, "an honorable man." What we are describing by the term criminoid is again a psychodynamic mechanism, a way of dealing with hostile impulses. This mechanism, like all the others, may play only a minor role in a personality or it may be of such proportional strength as to dominate it. It, too, may be latent, or reactive to unusual stress, or an occasional or permanent character trait.

At one end of the criminoid range is behavior that is so close to the directly criminal that it is transitional between these two types. This would be exemplified by the man whose inner restraints and defenses are such that he cannot himself kill anyone but can arrange for another to commit such an act. At the opposite extreme are minor manipulations that are within the law, injure no single person directly, and are often valued as being "smart." The dual conscience of some businessmen has frequently been described—he who would never personally harm the poor widow and her children but as a business matter will foreclose their mortgage to his own profit. Similarly, several decades ago it was not uncommon economic practice to exploit immigrant workers through forcing them to rent poorly constructed company houses and to buy goods, often inferior, priced and sold by company stores. Labor unions, as they have grown in power, also have tolerated forms of blackmail and racketeering. The treatment of migrant workers must be mentioned here too as an example of injurious criminoid behavior on the part of some industries.

Overt criminality is generally all too evident as such, and neurotic behavior is increasingly attracting recognition. But criminoid behavior, masked and camouflaged as it is in individuals, eludes notice and has not been defined and brought into focus. This is somewhat surprising because when it is widespread it is quickly recognized as corruption. Its ability to elude investigation is probably related to the fact that the criminoid mechanism permeates so many of our attitudes. We tend to avoid thinking of accepted criminoid activity in moral terms. "Oh, don't be naive, that's done every day—politics (or business, or labor, or human nature) is like that," we say. In the statistical sense of average, criminoid behavior may even be "normal." But just because it is normal in India to get smallpox or in America to get dental caries, does not mean that these conditions are any less of a disease or problem. They are not normal in the sense of healthy. In fact, the acceptance of the criminoid as normal makes him even more of a serious threat to our society.

Let us now look at who some criminoids are. In politics there are the demagogues and hate-mongers, those leaders and groups who seek gain at the expense of others. Usually they are extremists (right or left) who try to discredit and paralyze the moderates, and bring on overt violence. There often seems to be an appalling affinity between politics and criminoid behavior. The public official who uses his cloak of authority to protect underworld activities in exchange for various kinds of gratuities is a routine fixture on the political scene. But let us make no mistake, corrupt politicians and their accomplices do not have exclusive rights to this kind of acting out. Hundreds of thousands if not millions of apparently stable men and women avidly support demagogues advocating violence and hatred, if some reasonably good rationalizations can be found. Pressure groups out to serve exclusively their own selfish ends act upon government to secure their goals regardless of the welfare of others, sometimes even pressing for war. Such behavior may be normal, in the sense of average, in the political and economic life of society. But our measuring rod for a society is not statistical, it is psychological and biological. It is a scale of emotional maturity derived from observing the contrast between the egocentric, hostility-prone attitudes of the mistreated infant and the outgoing givingness of the adult of good will.

Criminoid mechanisms may be prominent in the lives of many persons without being recognized consciously by themselves or the people involved with them. Few people aid criminoids with a view to doing harm deliberately and maliciously; most people simply do not know any better, and some even think of themselves as being quite virtuous.

To illustrate how this operates on a different level let us note briefly the case of Steve, a young man of high caliber. He was quite mature in his capacity for love and sympathy and would not knowingly hurt anyone in any way. Steve had strong feelings of inferiority as a result of overprotection by his mother during childhood. Insecure in his masculinity, he believed in sincere good faith that a young man of any virility should prove himself by, as he said, "getting women." Being attractive and highly motivated sexually, he seduced, lived with, and then abandoned many girls, causing some of them serious unhappiness. Yet Steve was only doing what he thought was expected of a "real man." Only when he learned the nature of maturity and saw realistically what he had been doing, was he able to find less criminoid, more adult modes of expressing his hostility and his masculinity.

In our society a great many people understand democracy and freedom to be a license for grabbing something away from the unwitting next guy, despite the cost to him. This is done under the admirable guise of pursuing success, the endless and ruthless search for the American dream. But success is not a purely egocentric matter. If it were, the very biosocial foundation of society would be dangerously undermined and probably destroyed, as it yet may be. True success is measured by constructiveness, by contributing to the well-being and happiness of others. Success in any field is measured by the excellence of the person's responsible contribution, what he has given to others, be it for their safety, or their entertainment, or for the advance of the human spirit. The tiny infant is egocentric, even parasitic, but then its sole task is its own development; but society is our sole means of security against nature. Our health, pleasure, and survival are made possible only by society through the contributions of each adult.

When an individual's self-love is too strong, it is very apt to lead him into criminoid behavior, however righteous he may seem to himself in his own self-image. Through his impatience for personal success he is apt to sacrifice the very rewards for which he burns himself out. More hostility is then aroused and this hostility (as does all hostility), in turn, seeks some person or group to hate—a scapegoat. Demagogues rise to power by offering objects for this hate. Rationalizations are readily found. And thus the criminoid mechanism becomes widespread.

Not all criminoids are important leaders. For example, let us look at the case of a small-town woman, raised in a modest, middle-class family. At eighteen Joan married the town "catch," the only son of a well-to-do real-estate broker. The young man, unlike his father and wife, was not very aggressive about work, his chief ambition being to write a history of the area in which they lived. Thus Carl preferred poring over the early settlers' records to buying and selling property for his contemporaries.

At first his wife was content with her marriage. The business continued to thrive under her father-in-law's direction and the income from it and Joan's position in the town satisfied her needs to be first and favored.

Then, however, the general economy of the country slowed down dramatically, Carl's father died, and the business fell in danger of going under. Carl forsook his career as a historian and devoted himself unflaggingly to the business in an effort not only to maintain financial security for his family, but even beyond this to satisfy his wife's needs for social prestige. It was an uphill fight. Increasingly frustrated by lack of money and success, Joan began to taunt and blame her husband to his friends behind his back, meanwhile showing him a contempt and coldness that gradually undermined his stamina and his self-respect. Mounting but repressed rage at his wife made Carl anxious and depressed and he began to drink and to neglect the children. Tensions in the home only increased, and Carl drank more and more heavily. In desperation he attempted suicide. Now his wife rejected him totally. His reputation was ruined. He had no one to turn to. Carl was not sufficiently mature to handle matters, and soon afterwards he developed mild schizophrenic symptoms. The situation became such that he had to be committed to a state hospital.

Joan, far from standing by Carl when he needed her and when she could have helped to save him and thus have kept a father for her children, was glad to be rid of him and to be free to pursue her ambitions unhampered. As the economy improved and times generally got a bit better, Joan advanced in a store where she found a position, and after some years she became assistant to the manager. The children had a difficult time, for the relief of the tension between their parents was bought at the price of losing their father, who was their chief emotional support and thereby their only model for good human relationships. Joan was callously indifferent to them. She entrusted their care to what hired help she could find and, when this failed, she would often lock them in separate rooms, tying the youngest to a chair to keep him out of mischief. Both children developed nightmares and a variety of behavior problems that signified the inevitable fears and arousal of excessive hostility and the warping of their development.

Joan's relationship to society was similar in feeling. Though desirous of respect in the community and very charming on the surface in her business and social relations, she inwardly despised all those who were beneath her socially. True to type she fawned upon those whom she saw as stepping stones. Where she worked she tacitly encouraged certain excessively harsh and unethical practices, and in the community she strove to keep minority groups off all local committees. Once after having had a few cocktails at a party she revealed that she believed blacks and Jews should be deported wholesale or else exterminated.

On the whole, however, this woman's behavior would not be considered criminal, and most of her intimates would not have considered her antisocial. She could quite righteously justify her actions. The hostility behind them was, for the most part, indirect. The fact that it helped to ruin the lives of her husband and her children was considered only a family matter. Her civic attitudes were considered her own business. Joan's behavior was not in any way illegal and so no one could step in to check her without being accused of meddling in purely private affairs.

But the criminoid nature of this woman is obvious and the lack of neurosis (in the narrower sense of the specific symptoms) probably shows best in the fact that she could not only behave the way she did but could do so without accumulating any really effective feelings of guilt. If she had had more of a conscience, more internal checks, she could not have acted out her hostilities to such an extent, even in this indirect form. So much guilt would have built up that Joan would have been forced into some type of emotional or psychosomatic disturbance. The hostility, like heat or water, would have been forced under pressure into other paths.

Other families have broken up during periods of severe economic distress; other women have been forced to work under conditions less than optimum for their children. Too, the kinds (though perhaps not the intensity) of prejudices that Joan held are not unusual in towns where class lines are rigidly drawn. But this woman did not merely reflect the attitudes of a family or group situation; nor did all members of her group accept such attitudes nor behave as she did.

Criminoid groups are analogous to crime areas. We have already noted that a certain percentage of boys in crime areas do not go along with the gangs. Joan's social group might have provided the temptation, opportunity, and encouragement for some of the criminoid behavior in which she indulged. But there must have been something in her own motivations that led her to the particular patterns with which she handled her hostilities. In brief outline, these inner motivations and the early influences that shaped them were as follows.

Joan's mother had also been a beautiful girl, without education but deeply ambitious "to amount to something," as she incessantly proclaimed. Disappointed in her marriage to a shiftless man, she had never really wanted children but when Joan was born, the woman was determined that this child should realize all the goals she herself had not achieved. Increasingly neglected by her husband, she drilled her daughter in dress and deportment, and took domestic jobs so that her child might have voice and piano lessons. But she did not give Joan the two great essentials: unselfish love and respect for the child's own personality. The father also resented the child, seeing her as an emotional and financial drain.

As the child was shaped, so the woman became. Following the pattern of her own and her mother's reactions to the father, Joan felt only contempt for men, and her fine social manners covered the hatred and rebellion she felt against the depriving, dominating mother who had imposed these manners upon her.

It is a general fact that an adult behaves toward others in later life according to two chief responses to his parents: (1) he identifies with the parent and acts as the parent did during the person's childhood; and (2) he reacts toward other people with the same feelings he had toward his parents as objects. Usually, probably always, there is some mixture of these two; that is, there is simultaneously identification with, and object relations to, the parent.

Joan, identifying with her mother, tended to treat her husband and children as her mother had treated her father and herself. She turned away from her husband when he failed to live up to her expectations; and she neglected her children (as her mother had neglected her) for the pursuit of the goals her mother had instilled within her. But Joan also harbored feelings of revenge against her parents, and, in retaliation, lived out toward her husband the hate and rejection she had felt toward her father and mother. Her capacity to love, to feel good will toward others, was crippled by this lifelong, repressed resentment for the lack of love and understanding during her childhood and for the disregard of her own personality under the imposition of her mother's ambitions. Beneath her surface conformity there burned to a pathological extent constant and intense hostility.

Why did these hostilities not come out more openly? Probably because there had not been a model for naked cruelty and violence in Joan's upbringing to enable her to indulge in this directly herself. She was raised to be a perfect lady, and her parents were always models of correct behavior. Instead, the pent-up feelings were forced into other channels, perhaps no less harmful, but not as overt. Viruses are such tiny organisms that they cannot be seen under the usual microscope, as bacteria can. Yet the viruses can produce in our bodies just as serious diseases as the relatively large bacteria. Indeed, just because they are so small, they elude direct study and hence are today the more dangerous enemy of man. Like these viruses, the hostility that finds expression in criminoid form through masked interpersonal and group cruelties may achieve ends just as destructive as frank criminality, which, like bacteria, is at least open for all to see.

As we have pointed out before, the differences among the various hostilodynamic mechanisms are based not only upon the form and intensity of the hostility and its mixture with other motivations, but also on how the hostility is handled by the ego and superego. In the neurotic criminal, to whom we now turn our attention, hostile, antisocial impulses break through into behavior, but they do so only against strong opposition from the individual's judgment and conscience. These ego and superego influences operate in various ways, two of which deserve special mention here.

In one type of case, the inner operation from the superego is quite thoroughly repressed and is not conscious. The ego consciously accepts the antisocial impulses and the individual appears to himself and to others as an unalloyed criminal character. Ostensibly, he approves of this in himself and in his acts; but meanwhile his conscience, though it operates without his awareness, has grown more and more powerful, grinding away silently but no less effectively. This is the sort of criminal who repeatedly gets caught or otherwise manages to bring suffering on himself; this is someone who—like Lady Macbeth—can freely plan and initiate murder, apparently with the most complete determination and no conflict at all, but, after the deed, finds himself shaken with guilt, which may be quite unconscious, and brings about self-punishment.

Andy exemplifies this kind of neurotic criminal. He was the first child born to a fortyish, middle-class salesman and his young wife. The father was a large, husky, aggressive, and talkative man who had completed college and was always very ambitious to achieve financial success. He enjoyed people and parties, and his alcohol consumption gradually increased until it became a fairly serious problem. His temper had a short fuse and could easily be triggered, especially when he was drinking. Andy's mother appeared to be a sweet, immature, and insecure woman. She felt that her problems would be solved by her marriage to this older, seemingly secure, and knowledgeable man. She had finished high school and worked as a salesgirl in a department store. She had a beautiful, enchanting face, which tended to make you less aware of her basic immaturity. She had never felt very close to her parents and was needy for physical affection. She was twenty-one when Andy was born. It must have been a totally perplexing experience for her to be a mother —it was simply not like having your own doll to play with. From the start things did not seem to go right with Andy. Breast feeding did not work and he did not do all that well on the bottle either. He seemed to cry all the time and his mother never could figure out what to do to quiet him. She even tried spanking him before he was a year old, but this only served to make him cry louder and more vigorously. Andy's father was away traveling for his job much of the time and so could offer little help. When he was home he was usually rather irritated about the situation there anyway; his wife was always yelling or complaining about Andy, who was often crying.

Although Andy's mother really did not want any more children, her husband convinced her that having another might make Andy happy. So Lisa was born when Andy was three. She did seem like a very different baby from the first. She loved her bottle, never cried much, and slept regularly and well. Andy remained difficult.

Andy's earliest memories show a kind of early bleakness in his life. It was clear to him that Lisa was the favored child. He was frequently punished but she never was. He quickly learned that both parents were moody and unpredictable. Some days almost everything he did was wrong and his mother would scream at him and slap him. She repeatedly let him know that he was a bad boy who would never amount to much. His father gradually realized how unfair his wife's treatment of Andy was and he would bitterly reprimand her for it. This meant that Andy might have this argument between his parents used against him because his mother would wait until the father was on the road and then she would beat the boy, seeking revenge for his having turned her husband against her. The woman's treatment of Andy became increasingly cruel as time went on. One day when he was five he got his new pants dirty while playing outdoors. Her punishment was to fill the bathtub with cold water and have him lie in it for half an hour with his clothes on. Andy was too frightened of his mother at this point to even report this incident to his father. Now he knew better than to incur her wrath by having his father stand up for him.

By the time he entered school, Andy was subdued and submissive. He also was very bright and never had any difficulty with schoolwork. Although his grades were usually good enough, Andy seemed to spend a lot of time daydreaming. Another telling indicator that something was wrong was that he failed to make any friends at all. He read a great deal, especially science fiction books. His parents continued to get along poorly and an unplanned daughter was born when Andy was seven.

By the fourth grade, Andy's teachers felt that psychological tests should be ordered because of the boy's atypical behavior. It was noted that

> Andy is a cooperative nine-year-old boy who was overly serious in his approach to the tests. He is a very methodical worker, and throughout the testing period there were many evidences of compulsivity and overcontrol. He tried desperately to work to the best of his ability. However, he had to be reassured and praised constantly. He criticized his productions and was unduly disturbed over any failures. He appeared eager to please, and in fact went to extremes to gain acceptance and praise from the examiner. Personality and projective test results indicate that Andy has a very poor self-concept and that he feels extremely discouraged in the home situation, where he thinks he is receiving very little warmth and understanding. In order to satisfy some of his needs, Andy has resorted to much fantasizing. He also has a great amount of hostility, which he turns inward. He has many feelings of isolation and helplessness in his present situation, and these are coupled with feelings of inferiority and inadequacy. Andy thinks things are hopeless and he feels frustrated.

It was recommended that Andy and his parents accept a referral to a child guidance clinic. The father wanted to go, but because he was away from home so much he really was not able to arrange it. His wife, on the other hand, felt guilty and angry and refused to go for professional help. She felt it would just make her feel worse.

By the time Andy was in sixth grade his overt behavior had seriously deteriorated. He started smoking cigarettes and stealing money at home and at school. His parents were separated by now and he lived with his two sisters at home with their father. Since the father still had to travel for his job, he hired a series of housekeepers to care for the children. None of these women were effectual when it came to Andy and he regularly took advantage of them. By the seventh grade he had been suspended several times from school. He joined forces with a group of young hoodlums from another school and they formed a gang. They terrorized many local neighborhoods and their activities became well-known to the police. Seldom, however, were any of the boys actually caught. They were clever thieves and muggers who constantly moved to new locations. Andy's father tried everything to get the boy to stop his criminal acting out. But neither reason, nor threats, nor even severe punishment, including physical beatings, had any effect on Andy. He would promise to change but never did.

Psychiatric treatment was tried when Andy was fifteen and on probation with the juvenile authorities. By this time he had started using drugs. In psychiatric interviews Andy would be pleasant and agreeable if he were talking about what he wanted to discuss—which was mainly drugs or his antiestablishment feelings. However, any attempt at confrontation, that is, at insight or the facing of realities, would result in his walking out or yelling at the psychiatrist in an abusive fashion. Once Andy even stole the psychiatrist's prescription pad and forged his name to obtain barbiturates. This young man had been sent for treatment, but he had no motivation for it, no desire to change in any way.

His father had remarried by now to a kindly woman who had been widowed and had four children of her own. She genuinely tried to understand and help Andy but he rejected outright all her overtures. If she even asked him to pick up his clothes, which he typically left on the floor of his room, he would shout tirades of abuse at her and stomp out of the house with clenched fists. The woman lived in daily fear that Andy would get one of her children started on drugs. It was finally decided that because of his uncontrollable use of drugs it would be impossible for Andy to continue in out-patient psychotherapy and that he could no longer remain at home. His family was given the option of committing him either to a correctional institution for juvenile delinquents or to the adolescent unit of a state psychiatric hospital. They chose the hospital. Andy failed to use the drug rehabilitation program effectively and instead made the hospital the base for continuance of his drug use.

After he had been at the hospital for six months, Andy hung himself in his room. He had harbored a deep and abiding hatred of himself, though you would not have known this when you first spoke with him. On the surface he seemed bright, friendly, alert, and he actually had many fascinating ideas. These had to do especially with how society should be restructured so the "bad guys" would not be on top and the "good guys" squashed under their heels. Who were these bad guys? Well, they were the ones who ran things, like parents, teachers, doctors, lawyers, politicians, policemen, in fact, maybe all adults, all authorities. The good guys, naturally, were the kids who wanted their freedom and independence to be themselves, to do their own thing and to build a so-called better world. So far his theme did not sound too different from that proffered by many idealistic young people who rebel against the establishment. However, it was different with Andy because his hostility was so intense that it had solidified into a hatred that demanded that he strike out against society. This meant stealing, mugging, fighting, drug abuse, and the like. But at the same time that he engaged in these criminal activities, Andy's internal checks were operating and causing considerable unconscious conflicts for him. More and more his hostilities came to be directed away from society toward himself. In the three months prior to his suicide, Andy's intake of drugs increased dramatically and it is rather surprising that he didn't kill himself in this way. His hostilities against himself, originating in the superego as guilt, were so intense that they had to be vented somehow. His superego simply reflected them back upon himself.

In a second type of neurotic criminal the superego forces are much more conscious, although, like the unwilling alcoholic, they are not sufficiently powerful to alter or control the patterns of the individual's behavior. His ego judges it harshly; he knows that it does not conform to his own or society's standards and he may even seek psychiatric treatment in an effort to change. But meanwhile, his need for punishment is great. Tim, an accountant in his early thirties who came for treatment after serving a prison term for embezzlement, was just such a neurotic criminal. He was a family man with a wife and two children, a kindly husband and father who enjoyed his home to the full.

With high intelligence, a quick wit, and a most personable appearance, Tim had no difficulty in inspiring confidence and obtaining excellent positions. He always gravitated to rather high-level jobs in which he was responsible for considerable sums of money. For a while Tim would function with complete reliability, but soon after establishing himself he would begin to devise clever methods of embezzlement. These would succeed for a while, but then, inevitably, he would find himself on the brink of discovery. In desperation he would struggle to hide his acts; Tim would plead with his wife and friends to help him raise funds to cover what he had taken. Swearing that this was the last time he would do such a thing, he was so convincing, so pitiable, so desperately anxious to save his family from disgrace, that he repeatedly succeeded in extracting sufficient funds from others to cover what he had stolen. This was his pattern, his "fate neurosis," and while Tim struggled heroically to free himself from its compulsion, the power of his early conditioning was such that he found himself repeating it again and again. Because he did not accept his criminal motivations but fought against and was tormented by these childish residues, his most prominent dynamic mechanism was that of the neurotic criminal.

Tim was one of those children who was unwanted from the moment of conception. His parents' marriage forever hovered on the brink of divorce. Tim's mother and father lived together in a state of armed truce, hostile to each other and escaping from each other into outside interests as much as possible. It was in this ungiving, unloving world of his childhood that Tim learned to manipulate others. It was only through wit, charm, and cajolery that he could achieve any attention and emotional satisfaction. The starving man finds food as best he can; the emotionally starved child struggles for love as best he can.

Many a child tries to stay his emotional hunger by consuming candy. Often he cannot refrain from filching it. Others demand such inadequate substitutes for love as toys or money, and these, too, such children are frequently unable to keep themselves from secretly appropriating. Tim's father sometimes gave him pennies, dimes, and nickels. This was not done in a setting of interested love and understanding, but rather in place of it. Nevertheless, so little attention did Tim get from his father that these gifts provided thrilling moments for him. He would literally dream about the small change and, when it was not forthcoming, he gradually learned how to remove it from his father's clothes without being detected.

Soon his whole quivering interplay of emotions began to cluster around this pilfering. The small change came to represent not only the love and concern he wanted from his parents, but also, by using it to treat his friends, the means for buying love. Through this act he also expressed the hatred against his parents that was engendered by their rejection of him, and by his behavior he courted punishment for this hatred. Of course, this tendency for self-punishment was not conscious to him as a child nor as an adult. Even as a grown man Tim was unable to face the pain of acknowledging to himself how unwanted he was and had been. All he was ever aware of both then and earlier was a Damoclean sense of impending doom, of some unknown sword hanging over him by a single hair. This latent guilt and need for punishment, no weaker (indeed probably stronger) because not conscious, provided yet another motive for his thefts. Each time he stole and was not caught he felt a greater reassurance, seeing in his escape the proof that fate, so often seen in the imago of the parents, had not after all really abandoned him.

Thus his neurotic criminal behavior came to express emotions too powerful to resist. This caused a true psychological addiction, which in others is more frequently fixed on food, cigarettes, gambling, or alcohol and wherein the hostility to self and others is typically silent and unconscious. In adult life Tim struggled against this. He was not, like the criminoid character, able to control the direct acting out of his antisocial impulses; but unlike the true criminal, he could not embrace and make a career out of them. Nor were his defenses strong enough to prevent the acting out of his warped, childhood emotional patterns, though they were strong enough to see to it that he punished himself with poignant suffering.

Chapter 8

PRIVATE MECHANISMS

For a long time the term *constitutional psychopathic inferiority* was used as a catch-all label for behavior disorders that would fit none of the other diagnostic categories. With increasing knowledge of the effects of early conditioning experiences and with the realization that there was no valid evidence to support the term *constitutional*, that part of the label was dropped, and the term psychopath was substituted. But as many of these individuals came to be studied psychodynamically, it was recognized that they were motivated by precisely the same emotional mechanisms that in other persons produce physical and psychological symptoms. But here the neurosis was expressed more in actual behavior than in thought, feeling, or bodily organs. Hence the term *neurotic character* came into use.

As we have noted, infantile impulses persist in everyone to some degree. If these have been patterned by basically good relationships and if they are balanced off by mature motivations, then they cause no difficulty. On the other hand, if they have been distorted by conditioning that was characterized by conflicts and if as a result the person suffered too much emotionally as infant and child, or if they have been so intensified that the mature developed is hampered, then they will disturb some aspect of the individual's functioning. The neurotic character differs from the criminal, the criminoid, and the neurotic criminal in that he defends himself against his infantile hostile impulses in such fashion that, though acted out, they appear only in indirect, disguised form. Essentially he suffers from a private neurosis in which the underlying hostility, while it may affect intimates and other individuals, is repressed and associated most prominently with self-induced punishment.

The example we shall present shows an underlying personality structure similar to that of Tim, one of the neurotic criminals described previously. The two histories, however, contrast in certain important details, which illustrate the specific quantitative role that early influences play in the choice of outcome.

Alex, an ambitious, highly intelligent young man, had lost his mother through death before he reached the age of one year. His father hired a nurse to care for him and gave the boy very little attention or companionship. Meanwhile the nurse answered any childish misbehavior by reminding the growing child that she was not his mother but was being paid for taking care of him and would leave if he did not act as he should. The combined rejection by both nurse and father filled Alex with resentment. Although in childhood, while the ego is weak, feeling is usually almost synonymous with action, this boy strove to repress all retaliative behavior because he desperately feared total abandonment.

How was Alex able to develop effective enough psychological defenses against his anger, induced by such treatment, to prevent him from acting out his hostile tendencies in the form of criminal behavior? Primarily there were two vital reasons. In the first place, in spite of the faulty upbringing the father and nurse did have considerable affection for the child. Alex's father loved his small son after the fashion of so many busy, self-centered men who find too little time to translate their interest into a real experience for a child. The nurse, too, notwithstanding her terrifying threats to leave, actually stayed on faithfully for many years and truly grew very fond of Alex. In the second place, as we have mentioned, this boy was so insecure that he dared not put into action his real resentful feelings. Any hostile behavior that would verge in the direction of the criminal was checked by love and by fear. Alex dared not act in any antisocial way for fear of losing what little emotional support he had, and also, because of loving and being loved to some degree, he repressed the impulses.

When a person hates those he also loves, guilt is probably inevitable. Two mechanisms can be distinguished here. One involves hostility originating from the id, which is pent up and turned against the self, presumably by the superego. The other mechanism involves hostility to the self, which originates in the superego—blaming oneself, and thus feeling guilt, for past deeds or current wishes. In the case of Alex this meant that pent-up anger toward his father and nurse was largely turned against himself. And, the inevitable guilt for his hostility then made him feel that he deserved to be rejected and that he was in reality just as bad as his father and nurse suspected. These motivations of hostility and guilt added a new dynamic to the boy's environment. In the emotional life the punishment fits the source—that is, punishment takes the form of whatever caused the anger. In this case the source or cause was rejection; it caused anger which caused guilt; the guilt led to a desire for punishment in the specific form of being rejected, which led Alex to unconsciously provoke rejection—a truly neurotic and vicious cycle.

As we all do, Alex grew up to expect from other adults the treatment he had received from those nearest him in childhood. He would enter into a friendship yearning for the loving attention he had always sought in vain. But soon he would feel that the other person (like his father and nurse) was not really interested in him and did not understand him. Then his underlying feelings of deprivation would be ignited and set off his anger. This appeared mostly in subtle reproaches against his friend, such as tacitly making him feel that he did not quite live up to expectations. The hostility toward himself came out by continuing these reproaches in such a way that the friend would actually lose patience with him. By thus provoking rejection, he reestablished the childhood pattern. When this occurred, as it did in childhood, Alex would complain to a new confidant about his disillusionment with and betrayal by the former friend. This complaining to another was the nearest he ever came to expressing any direct hostility to anyone other than himself.

Occasionally as he went through the cycle, Alex would in fact get himself so rejected in spite of conscious efforts to avoid it that the relationship would break off entirely. Usually, however, he would be able to continue a precarious contact, at least for a while, with the new confidant. And so the relationships of his adult life were of the same tenuous, ambivalent nature as his feelings toward his father and nurse in childhood.

This childhood pattern of turning from one to another repeated itself with friends in school and in a whole series of jobs. It also repeated itself with girls. He did marry, but in spite of every attempt to preserve the relationship, his wife grew wholly intolerant of Alex's petty and constantly fretful pattern of provocativeness as it emerged toward her. In the end she divorced him. With his ego-saving capacity for projection he convinced himself and also some others that the entire fault for the dissolution of the marriage lay with his wife. Alex complained of her egocentricity and inability to have any real interest in him. By this defense of projection he did not suffer directly from his guilt and kept tolerably comfortable.

In Alex hostility was rarely expressed in a direct way. For the most part it caused guilt and was turned against himself to harm his own life by making himself rejected and isolated, deprived of good, warm feelings for and from other persons. His behavior shows the mechanism of the neurotic character because, while consciously striving to get along with others in close gratifying relationships, his adult life was unconsciously lived for him by the child within himself. Alex was conditioned to this pattern of behavior during his earliest years. This emotional pattern eventuated in the way he lived rather than in specific psychological or physical symptoms, as is the case with the classic neuroses.

The term *neurotic*, taken in its broadest meaning, refers to any emotionally caused disorder resulting from influences during childhood that block and warp full development. According to this definition all the hostilodynamic mechanisms (except perhaps some instances of sublimation) would be considered various forms of neurotic disturbance. On the other hand, the word *neurosis* has been used in a restricted sense to apply only to certain symptoms and combinations of them (that is, syndromes), especially those designated as hysteria, phobias, and compulsion neurosis. These are the ones that were intensively studied and elucidated by Freud. The well-known mechanism of neurotic symptom formation is the disguised return from repression of strong, mostly infantile, emotional forces.

Because of the individual's mature drives, adult standards, training, and conscience, these infantile forces are controlled and denied direct expression. But such unrelieved tensions affect the normal mature thought, behavior, vegetative functioning, and even sensory perception; that is, they cause symptoms. If the forces of maturity and restraint are inadequate and cannot master or offset the infantile motivations, then we see the mechanisms of criminal acting out, of impulse-ridden behavior, of certain perversions, of masochism, and of similar deficiencies of mature control. This is not neurosis in the classic and narrow sense of repression by conscience and re-emergence of the repressed infantile impulses as symptoms, but it is neurosis in the broad sense of the same disturbed psychic forces being at work that result from the persistence of disordered childhood patterns.

To illustrate the dynamics of hostility in classic neurosis, we have selected a simple, relatively common type of case and, for variety, one where there is a strong reactive element. That is, in the following vignette the symptoms result from internal emotions that have been intensified by an external life situation.

A personable young woman, Dee, came for treatment, complaining of anxiety. This anxiety was without content—she did not know what she felt anxious about. But, nevertheless, Dee lived in a state of persistent fear and felt that this might portend some evil about to befall her family. She was married and had one child. The anxiety, it turned out, had developed in the course of pregnancy and became much more severe when Dee left the small town in which she was reared and came with her husband and new baby to live in the large urban center to which his work brought him. Dee's anxiety now had mounted to the point where she was quite unable to enjoy anything in her life, and she consequently began to fear that she was headed for a nervous breakdown.

The salient feature of her childhood was overprotection. Her parents had seen to it that everything was done for her; even as sne grew older ner life nad been a playtime with practically no responsibility. Both her father and mother were leading citizens in the town, and wherever their daughter went, she was welcomed and treated with deference. Dee knew "everyone" and "everyone" accepted and knew her.

When she married, however, a very common difficulty arose. Shortly after the baby was born, her husband was promoted and transferred. The only life Dee had known had been her entirely dependent, protected play-relationship to her parents and to the community in which she grew up. Now she was suddenly removed from this to become, far away, just one of millions. Naturally her husband could not provide all the emotional support that she had left behind. It was a rude awakening for the girl to find that he was not father, mother, and friends rolled into one but merely another person of her own generation who had to devote a great deal of time, energy, and interest to his job.

Not only was Dee's emotional intake suddenly diminished from a flood to a trickle by the geographic move, but in addition, for the first time in her life, she had to shoulder real responsibilities. Now she had a young baby with its enormous demands for attention and its relentless interference with her indulgence of herself. In addition to the baby, there was also the house to run, the problems of shopping, cooking, cleaning, and getting help, to say nothing of the harassments of budget. In other words, the emotional give-get balance had shifted—much less was coming in, much more was going out. Dee was like a little child abandoned by her parents and, to make matters even more difficult, she had to be a parent herself while trying to adjust to a new community.

She reacted, as do all animal organisms, with the fight-flight response. She thought of running home to mother; but much as she wanted to, Dee could not accept this path of action, jeopardizing as it would her marriage and the security of a home for her child, and running counter as it did to her healthy drives to maturity. With the possibility of flight cut off, she felt trapped and her anger mounted. However, the rage could not be expressed either; there was no pattern in her life for that. The anger pent up inside her was the danger that she sensed; but she was by no means aware of her emotional situation as we have described it. Dee did not think of herself consciously as a dependent, overprotected child. Neither did she realize the extent to which she protested against the responsibilities of husband, home, and baby, in a new, strange, and distant city.

Repressed hostility is perhaps the most common single cause of simple anxiety states (anxiety hysteria). At times Dee occasionally lost her temper with her husband, but that was about all the hostility that ever came to the surface. She would have been horrified at the idea of having any resentment against her husband or her child. Thus her own unexpressed rage caused the threat of impending doom.

This is a typical neurotic mechanism. The hostility is defended against and repressed and the individual does not behave violently or antisocially to gain revenge. But this hostility, which is apparently dismissed so effectively, does not simply dissipate and so lose its power. It generates a neurotic symptom: in this case, simple anxiety. This anxiety is basically only a personal symptom but it does affect those with whom the individual is intimate. An anxious wife, unable to enjoy her child and husband, feeling restricted in her activities, is no easy person to be with; the husband and the child both suffer. This indirect effect of a repressed motivation is what Freud called "the return of the repressed."

This type of case is seen so frequently that another characteristic feature is worth mentioning. The repressed hostility may return pointed inward against the person himself, and, directly or through generating unconscious guilt, create urges for self-punishment. Usually the individual then reacts by denying himself relief from the very responsibilities that he protests against. For example, the husband or friends see something of what is going on, as, vaguely, does the young woman herself. They urge her to get some help with house and baby, to get out more, to get her life into balance. But typically, as in the case with Dee, the anxiety prevents her from achieving the solution. She fears that if she is away something will befall her child. And, by similar motivation and thinking, she cuts herself off from the normal satisfactions of recreation, attention, and emotional support, which friendly contacts might yield. She becomes caught in a vicious circle: frustration, which leads to anger, which leads to guilt, which leads, again, to frustration. This is another example of how the punishment fits the source.

Throughout our discussion of human personality development, we have seen that man is a biological unit and that when he is under stress, either from internal or external sources, his functioning is affected. Because he is a well-integrated unit, such stresses are reacted to by the entire organism. In some cases, however, they disturb one area of functioning more than another. Insofar as the higher centers of the nervous system are affected, we see manifestations of abnormal perception, thought, feeling, or behavior, or any combination of these. And insofar as the autonomic nervous system is affected, we see disturbances in the vegetative organs, that is, psychosomatic symptoms. When disturbed emotionally, each individual reacts characteristically. One may burst out in a childish tantrum; another may be depressed; still another may develop a pain in his stomach, or an asthma attack, or heart trouble, or a headache. Any and all combinations of reactions and symptoms can occur in a given case, in all areas of functioning, from the highest intellectual level to the lowest. Even the fragility of certain cells of the blood, the lymphocytes, is reported to alter under stress, emotional or physical.

Psychosomatic is a term that is commonly used in the broad sense of meaning any physical symptoms in which emotions are of appreciable causal importance. At least three mechanisms can operate in the contributions of emotions to symptoms. In the first group are those symptoms that are dramatizations or symbolizations of emotionally charged ideas. An example would be Freud's famous one of the girl who repressed her guilt about making a misstep sexually but expressed it symbolically by dragging her foot. Such a mechanism is that of classic conversion hysteria.

In the second mechanism a particular emotional need is expressed through a particular organ. Franz Alexander is *Psychosomatic Medicine* portrays a fairly well established example of this: that of hunger for love being expressed through the stomach as hunger for food. Biohistorically, this derives from the child's nursing years when the intake of food is closely associated with the intake of love. Thereby these two hungers seem to become linked to each other through conditioning. Later in life, when the adult craves love, his stomach may react as though it were preparing to receive food. If the need for love is not satisfied and the individual is angered, the anger, too, can affect the functioning of the stomach. The whole interplay of emotions, then, influences that organ system that chiefly expresses the need.

A third mechanism is that in which the symptom is simply part of the body's normal physiological reaction. When a person or animal is angered, there is regularly, as part of his fight-flight response, an increase in the rate and forcefulness of his heartbeat and an elevation of his blood pressure. These subside, along with the rest of the physiology, when the danger or irritant is past. In some cases, however, these cardiovascular symptoms are observed to occur without adequate external stimulation. In at least some of these cases, they are found to be reactions to threats that arise from within. The readying of the physiology for the exertion of fight or flight, of course, occurs regardless of whether the threat, irritation, or frustration is from outside or inside.

This physiological arousal can be observed in full or, apparently and for not well-understood reasons, only in part. For example, an elevation of blood pressure may be seen but few or no other signs of physiological overactivity appear. In such cases (of essential hypertension) preliminary studies suggest that these persons are usually in a state of intense, constant rage which, although near the surface, is typically well controlled so that their manner may be pleasant and gentle. This was the case with Tom. He was the oldest of six children. He had been spoiled and dominated by his mother, who also dominated Tom's physically strong father. When Tom was about ten years old the family lost all its money and possessions in a fire. Because of the resulting dire financial circumstances, Tom's mother forced the boy to get a job after school and on weekends. He reacted with bitterness for being thus prematurely forced to work. He resented tremendously having to give up the extreme spoiling that had characterized his earlier childhood.

Tom's mother was, in her dominance, an extremely overprotective woman. She forbade sports as dangerous, and later she even refused to allow Tom to see girls other than those of his own religious faith, who in his very small town tended to be rather reserved (if not actually repressed) socially. He obeyed despite the envy he felt of other boys who freely engaged in athletics and in sexual play with girls. Tom's mother set him the ideal of wealth and inspired him with excessive ambitions and great expectations. The woman was so domineering that she even managed to force Tom into a marriage with a girl of her own choosing. Thus Tom's whole life, his work, his religion, his marriage, came to mean submission to his mother. He tried in vain for many years to escape or rebel against this unconscious submissive attachment to his mother, but she was a powerful adversary. Finally Tom did divorce his wife, whom he never really loved, and then he plunged himself into sexual promiscuity and alcoholism. At one point he even took a girl to the Orient with him in a vain effort to escape his fears and achieve sexual and emotional freedom. For Tom, drinking and promiscuity were symbols of defiance against convention (which symbolized his mother) as well as a means of escaping from dependence and submissiveness (which was ingrained in him by her). However, these indulgences gave rise to feelings of deep guilt and anxiety and he was soon forced to abandon the rebellion. Tom's hypertension always increased markedly during these periods in which anxiety frustrated his attempts at heterosexuality.

Apparently in an effort to escape the conflict with his domineering mother, Tom as a child turned to his father. However, the unconscious masculine competitiveness with his father was intense, encouraged as it was by his mother, who made Tom feel that he was much better than his father. Tom reported dreams of direct sexual advances toward his mother. Evidently the woman had been seductive as well as dominating, and this served to intensify Tom's feelings of inferiority and hostility to his father. This drove him to further dependence upon his mother and to an anxious, submissive, masochistic attitude toward his father. While it is true that on the surface his relations with men were less acutely disturbing, the dependence and submissiveness toward them was even more intolerable than toward women. Again, Tom yearned to rebel. This was most clearly in evidence in his relationship with his boss. For example, Tom would take orders from the man with complete obedience, but then he would feel rebellious and hostile and on the verge of attacking his boss physically. Tom claimed that he fought a desperate battle with himself against "bending the knee" to his boss. Not surprisingly, this was precisely the phrase he used in describing his submissiveness to his mother: "I was always bending the knee to her." His rage at his mother was conscious and at his boss nearly so, though he knew nothing of the source of his feelings.

Besides his hostility from rebellion against his dependence and submissiveness, Tom would rage at not getting the passive receptive satisfaction he demanded, that is, at having to work hard and unremittingly as he was trained to do by his mother so prematurely as a child and thus never having been able to indulge his desires to be dependent on others. This rage, however, was never expressed directly; Tom was always quiet and gentlemanly. He dared not express his hostility for fear of losing the love of those around him. Until feelings of anxiety and guilt would overwhelm him, Tom would express his defiance privately in short-lived indulgences in promiscuity and solitary drinking. These activities were compulsive reactions to situations in which Tom overtly submitted to a man or woman and dared not defy them openly.

Tom was chronically pessimistic, anxious, and mildly depressed. He struggled against strong wishes to be in second place—passive, submissive, dependent—and at the same time he was in a perpetual state of rebellion against these wishes, since his pride demanded that he be first—independent and responsible. Although his hostility was successfully inhibited and thus found no sufficient outlet in behavior, it was not adequately bound in an organized chronic neurosis (for example, paranoia, compulsion neurosis, or chronic alcoholism). Cases not unlike Tom's have been reported in which the hypertension disappears when the patient develops neurotic symptoms. Tom was unable to accept and satisfy either his flight into his passive dependent wishes or his fight as hostile impulses. Consequently he was neither weak and dependent nor aggressively hostile—both were blocked in both directions. During periods when either trend was more satisfied, Tom's blood pressure was notably lower. As we have seen, Tom's hostility was defended against and repressed psychologically, but it affected his physiology.

This hostilodynamic mechanism of psychosomatic disorder seems to be ubiquitous. Who has never felt an anger within him make his heart pound, his color change, stomach and bowels tense up? Who has never noticed that illness in himself and others occur during periods of emotional stress? Hostility in one form or another seems to be of critical importance in many bodily conditions. Some epileptic attacks are apparently massive discharges of rage through muscular convulsions. Hostility seems to play a role, at least in part, in certain cases of hyperthyroidism and diabetes and indeed to some extent (probably because of being part of the fight-flight reaction) in most, if not all, disturbances of the physiology that are caused by emotional strains. Here is a case of how it affected a patient suffering with a peptic ulcer.

Julie, a college student, was appealing, intelligent, and quick to gain insight into her problem. A flare-up of the ulcer from which she suffered since she was fourteen brought her in for treatment, but it rapidly became clear that what was chiefly disturbing her was unconscious, inner rage.

Her father, to whom she was deeply attached, had died when she was thirteen. This necessitated the mother's obtaining a job in order to support her three children—the patient, a younger sister, and an older brother. When an opportunity was offered the mother in the small town where she had been raised, she took the children there and began a new life. Thus, precipitously, Julie lost not only her favorite parent but also her close friends and her whole school environment, all of which meant a great deal to her. Meanwhile, her relationship with her mother, which had never been close, was now severely strained. Julie's mother, through the loss of her husband and through the emotional drain involved in suddenly having to earn a living, was herself under great stress. Frustrated, uprooted, and lonely, Julie became irritable and withdrawn—fight and flight.

At about the same time she also developed the stomach trouble. Her physical condition declined as her emotional situation worsened until she finally suffered a gastric hemorrhage. Julie was rushed to the hospital, where it was found that she had a peptic ulcer. Under strict medical supervision she improved. Her mother, meanwhile, was by now feeling more secure and she could see that Julie was unable to make an adjustment in the new town. With the help of a scholarship fund, she decided to send Julie to boarding school. Here Julie became much happier and had no further trouble with her stomach until she left to go to college. This move again meant leaving old friends and the security of established ties. Julie still felt ill at ease with her mother and was unable to talk over her personal problems at home. Her shyness made it difficult for the other students to get to know her. And so once again she was cut off from her dependent attachments. Her longings were frustrated and intensified and the old reaction occurred—inner rage, withdrawal, and flare-up of the ulcer.

Needless to say, not all ulcers or other physical symptoms are caused by emotional factors alone. In this case, however, the evidence was cogent: even such a small thing as a disappointing letter from her mother or mild rejection by an acquaintance would precipitate abdominal pain of varying degrees of severity.

Julie obtained marked relief after a few interviews with the psychiatrist, for she became rapidly aware of what was going on in her emotions. For the first time in her life she began to face frankly her deep-seated needs for love and dependence and the hostility aroused in her by the frustration of these needs. She had not realized the amount of anger that was concealed beneath her sense of being lonely and shy. Directed mostly against her mother, it had been too full of conflict for Julie to face. As she began to become acquainted with these feelings, the conflict moved, as it were, from the physiological level up to the psychological. Instead of being reflected in her stomach, her problem became a matter of comprehensible reactions that she could now understand, deal with, and begin to solve. The hostility, too, so long unacknowledged, could be faced as a psychological problem and as a force within herself that did no good and much harm. The hostility could be reduced by understanding its sources and shifting the attitudes that underlay them. This is not always achieved by insight alone but may require systematic reconditioning by psychodynamically based psychotherapy to correct the childhood pattern.

Chapter 9

SOCIAL MECHANISMS

The term *sublimation* was introduced by Freud to signify the transformation of crude, animalistic impulses into socially acceptable and useful drives. As first used by him it applied chiefly to the libidinal impulses. For example, love, however physical its nucleus, can become the kind of love that is felt toward parent, child, country, humanity, and it can be expressed in literature and art. There is, of course, no reason why sublimation should be limited to libidinal impulses. Even direct hostility can be rerouted or transformed within the personality so that it motivates action devoted to the welfare of others. This can occur in a variety of ways.

Freely accepted, overt hostility can be used to attack social evils such as crime or tyranny; or, it can be used in the defense of home and family. Here the destructive impulse may be retained in its original form and acted out, but its aim is prohuman and

constructive. Albert Einstein, for example, who all his life avow-
edly detested the idea of war and violence, disappointed many
organized pacifists when he favored war against Nazi Germany.
He did so, he said, because he felt Nazism was something worse
than war.

Secondly, the hostility may not be overt nor expressed in an
open fashion, but may be verbal and intellectual rather than
physical. To distinguish it more clearly from our first example
above, contrast the commando or police officer with such a crusader for human rights as Dorothea Lynde Dix. Though physically frail and ailing, she stumped the country, storming the cita-
dels of authority with rousing speeches against those who mal-
treated the mentally ill. In like manner, Florence Nightingale
was hostilely aggressive in battling for proper medical and nursing care for British soldiers. Another illustration of sublimation
of hostility is the well-known dodge of giving little Willie, who is
smashing the furniture, nails and wood so he can hammer just
as freely, but constructively instead of destructively.

Thirdly, hostility that is unconscious and in no way evident
may generate overcompensatory attitudes or acts of good will
which betray their source only when analyzed. This compensa-
tory reaction may be quite successful; it is a mechanism that can
contribute to such socially useful work as surgery or other humanitarian activities. The surgeon, in addition to his mature
motivations, unconsciously may, in certain instances, satisfy
hostile feelings by cutting human beings, even though, like all
physicians, he does his work in the service of relieving suffering
and prolonging life.

Dynamically speaking, perhaps only the crusader mechanism
represents true sublimation in the most precise sense. There is in
the others some mixture of rationalization—that is, an ostensi-
ble (and often a good) reason masks the deeper motivations.
This must be distinguished from true sublimation. For instance,
conscious rationalization is a well known and frequently used
mechanism in international affairs. There are countless examples throughout history of wars being rationalized by an attack-
er who consciously and deliberately devised reasons to justify his
armed hostile aggression.

The following vignette illustrates sublimation, the hostility here being coupled with a mature drive of responsibility. Martha, a young woman lawyer, was married and had two children. She could boast of an excellent private practice and was famous for her work among the poor. Not only did she extend them professional aid, but she made many personal sacrifices on their behalf, sometimes involving her own family. This drive stemmed in large part from a mature wish to use her own powers and fortunate position to improve the lot of others. Reinforcing this, however, were a number of childish impulses, including a considerable amount of hostility.

Both the drive for responsibility and the feelings of hostility had their origins in her childhood. Martha had lost her mother when she was six. This left her, an only girl, with her father and two small brothers; and the father soon came to use her all he could in the care of these younger children. About this she had mixed feelings; in part she deeply resented the burden, but in part it gave her a sense of superiority. There was, of course, considerable hostility to the boys, not only because of having to care for them when she wanted to be free like other girls her age, but also because of rivalry for the attention of her father. Martha felt an intense need to be the first in her father's affection and to hold a favored place as the oldest child against the competition of her younger brothers. During the day she managed to put up a brave front, but at night, when she was alone, she would weep, look up at the stars in search of her mother, and feel very small, needy, poor, and forlorn.

Two mechanisms shaped themselves during these years. First, an identification of herself with people who were burdened with responsibilities beyond their ability, people who struggled beyond their strength. The second was overcompensation for her competitive-resentful hostility against such weaklings.

These two mechanisms developed this way: Martha did not dare show any anger toward her brothers or father for fear of losing her father's approval. As a defense she exaggerated her maternal feelings and behavior toward her brothers. Like herself, the boys were destitute of a giving mother and so by identifying with them she was able to enjoy some of the help she gave, vicariously, as though it were help received. Meanwhile, Martha let out her hostility through her need to be superior and to keep the boys in tow. Through these two devices she gained much satisfaction.

In Martha's adult life both these patterns operated in a similar way. In helping the poor she could prove herself secure, worthy of admiration, and well placed. Meanwhile she could also satisfy her hostile impulses in an overcompensatory, kindly way through her role as a superior with authority. The total result was a constructive contribution to the welfare of others although largely supported by sublimated hostility.

Part Four

SOCIAL AND
POLITICAL ATTITUDES

Chapter 10

HOSTILITY AND LOVE

A phylogenetic investigation into the origins of modern man, wherein you search particularly for clues to explain man's propensity to injure and kill his own kind, reveals that there are many and diverse reasons for his hostility. Some of these seem to be fundamentally rational and reactive, as when an herbivorous community of men requires salt for survival and another community unyieldingly holds the entire supply of that necessity within a confined geographical area. In contrast to this example, the reasons for the human sacrifices at seedtime are much less direct, involving as they do superstitions, and seem to arise from still obscure sources in man's emotional life. Serious attempts to penetrate beyond superficial explanations for man's hostility always seem to return to the very same identifying characteristic that gives mammals their name: the care and concern for their young, epitomized by the feeding breasts, the mammae of the nurturing, protecting mother.

Insofar as we are conscious of this deeply instinctive, protective care and nurture, it seems to be what we experience as parental love. It is so strong that a parent may willingly sacrifice his or her very life for the child and can barely face existence if the child should die. We also know from clinical experience that this powerful parental love is complemented by the child's even more powerful need for this love. And if it is not forthcoming, the child's whole emotional development to maturity is affected and usually seriously warped. Unwanted, rejected, neglected, or abused, the child goes through its entire life feeling deprived, frustrated, and inferior. And these feelings, as we have already noted, are then reacted to with the fight-flight response, which generates inner rage and hate and also regression.

Why then do we not see the same hostility, acted out or not, in other mammals. The answer is that we probably do. Recent studies by ethologists suggest that those other mammals that have a long period of dependence upon parents do in fact display psychological problems and hostile behavior when something has gone awry in their nurturing and therefore in their normal growth to maturity. In her fascinating book, *In the Shadow of Man*, ethologist Jane Goodall records her observations of chimpanzees and their society, which she has been studying closely in Tanzania for a number of years.

Because some of her observations are particularly relevant to our discussion at this point, they are presented here in some detail. First let us look at the case of Merlin, a three-year-old male chimpanzee. After the death of his mother, Marina, he was for all intents and purposes adopted by his six-year-old sister Miff. Despite her attentions toward her brother, various deteriorating changes in his appearance and behavior began to take shape.

> Merlin became more emaciated, his eyes sank deeper into their sockets, his hair grew dull and stringy. He became increasingly lethargic and played less and less frequently with the other youngsters. Also in other ways his behavior began to change. [By the time] he was four years old Merlin was far more submissive than other youngsters of that age: constantly he approached adults to ingratiate himself. At the

other end of the scale, Merlin was extra-aggressive to other infants of his own age group. When Flint [another young male chimpanzee] approached to try to play, Merlin, although he sometimes merely crouched or turned his back, was equally likely to hit out aggressively . . . As Merlin entered his sixth year his behavior was becoming rapidly more abnormal.

Before we draw any conclusions we must note by way of comparison the behavior of another orphaned chimpanzee.

Beatle lost her mother when she was about the same age as Merlin had been when Marina [his mother] died . . . Beatle showed similar signs of depression to those shown by Merlin: she too became rather emaciated, she too played less and less frequently. At about the time when Merlin's behavior had begun to deteriorate even more, however, Beatle's began to improve. . . . Both of these infants had been deprived of the reassurance of the breast. Both initially showed gradually increasing depression. Then Merlin's condition declined, whereas Beatle's improved. Beatle was able to continue riding about on another chimpanzee after her mother's death . . . once she scrambled aboard she was again in close physical contact with a large chimpanzee— an individual who knew what to do in times of trouble, who would rush her to safety up a tree at the right time, who could run fast and swiftly carry them both to safety.

Merlin, by contrast, had no haven of refuge after Marina's death. Miff was no more than a constant companion and was of little use to her brother in times of social excitement in the group. And so it seems possible that Merlin's troubles were principally psychological, that his terrible physical condition resulted more from a sense of social insecurity than from any nutritional deficiency.

Clearly, the cases of Merlin and Beatle represent examples of extreme interruptions in the normal pattern of parental care and consequently in the normal growth of the offspring to maturity. Nevertheless, the key feature differentiating the two cases is a telling one. What enabled Beatle to improve from her deteriorated condition following her mother's death would seem to be that she was provided with an effective mother substitute. Merlin was not. Miff could not assuage Merlin's feelings of insecurity and provide him with the continued nurturing care that he needed in order to grow properly into maturity.

Jane Goodall has studied other chimpanzees who, although not orphans, show disturbed behavior similar to that of Merlin.

> Flint's prolonged infancy was possibly due to Flo's extreme age, to the fact that she no longer had the strength to battle with her somewhat obstreperous child. . . . as Flint grew older he had taken to hitting and biting his mother when she refused him the breast—and although Flo had sometimes retaliated, she had at the same time held the child very close, as if trying to reassure him even while she bit or cuffed him . . . Flint was a bully to his old mother . . . When his sibling Flame was born Flint threw the most terrible tantrums if Flo did not immediately permit him to climb into their communal bed. As the weeks went by Flint's behavior began increasingly to resemble that of an orphaned youngster: he started to decline invitations to play . . . he became noticeably listless and lethargic.
>
> What went wrong with Flint's upbringing? Had he as a small infant been "spoiled" by too much attention from his mother, sister, and two big brothers? Whatever the reason for Flo's failure there can be no doubt but that Flint, today, is a very abnormal juvenile.

The love of the mother for her child is not only a model for love but for maturity. The mother and her young, in humans and in other species, represent the essence of maturity and immaturity, respectively. The offspring begins life as a single cell. While within the womb it is completely parasitic. At birth it has to learn suddenly at least to breathe for itself, and soon thereafter has to learn to swallow and take in food for itself. Gradually it gains the use of its senses, powers of locomotion; gradually it comes to be less utterly dependent upon the mother. The mother represents the complement of this. The more parasitic the infant, the more giving must be the parent. The child sucks up energies, for its goal is its own growth and development. The mother pours out energies, for her goal is now to assure the best development of her offspring—not for any tangible return, not to fulfill her ambitions, not for personal gain, but for the child's own sake. This is the essential of true maternal love and the pattern for true parental love also. It probably forms the core of all love—between the sexes and between friends.

This unselfish love of the mother for her child is also at the bottom of those feelings between human beings that make society possible. Human beings are not the only creatures to form societies. In fact almost all species do. What it is specifically that holds these species in societies is not yet well understood. No doubt it is a combination of many motives; but one powerful motive, as is evident from the study of human beings, lies in this capacity for love, which we see epitomized in the mother's relationship to the child. Identification with others as humans like ourselves probably has its source in this same love—in the mother's identification with her child and in the child's with its mother.

"Love thy neighbor" is an ideal of Western culture, an ideal which is, as we all know to our sadness, only partially achieved. Many people try to love but cannot. And when we come to examine why an individual is not able to love, we discover invariably that it is because he was not properly loved during the formative years of his childhood, that is, from conception to the age of about six or so. Perhaps he was not loved at all, perhaps he was loved not wisely but too well, but always something was wrong in the attitudes and feelings of the parents toward him during his tenderest years.

For example, Linda, twenty-one years old, was causing her parents much anguish because of her flamboyant sexual behavior and her repeated trouble with the law. Linda said she saw nothing wrong with it, but her parents could in no way reconcile themselves to her admission that she was having sexual affairs with several men, changing lovers every few weeks. They were shocked at her reckless and irresponsible way of life, and its flouting of convention. At her parent's insistence she finally agreed to see a psychiatrist, but it was clear that she capitulated only to silence their incessant pleas. Linda's attitude was very simple: she pointed out that she was young, that she did not want to get married and settle down, that she had strong sexual feelings and wishes for love, and that she did not see why she should not have her fun. Convention, she said, was outdated and hopelessly irrelevant, and she saw much to recommend freedom. Linda was very direct and forthright and superficially happy.

At first Linda discussed her parents with great objectivity; she said she loved them but felt they simply did not understand life. As she described her growing up, however, her dispassionate tone began to betray an underlying anger. She described her parents, especially her father, as being suspicious and impossibly strict in terms of standards of behavior. She said she felt under constant pressure from them and continually under the imposition of their ideas of what her life should be. Linda complained bitterly of their constant attempts to handpick her friends and her forms of recreation. While she lived at home they demanded exact obedience as to the hours she came in at night, and they always insisted on detailed accounts of where she had been and with whom.

It soon became apparent that it was in self-defense that she had developed a fight-flight reaction; without it, she felt unconsciously that she could not preserve the identity and independence of her own personality. The rebellion, of course, was aimed—again unconsciously—at the very heart of her parents' wishes for her. Since they tried to compel her to a rigid "goodness," she sought a defiant pattern of "badness" as an outlet for her hostility.

The parents' protectiveness was doubtless born out of love for their child, although a fearful sort of love. All children need some socialization, but Linda's parents did not win her over to what was good and reasonable through love, rather they sought to impose it upon her. It did not take long for Linda to learn that the chief motivation for her unconventional way of life was an unconscious form of rebellion against this imposition by which she asserted her independence and revenged herself on her parents. As Linda came to realize this she also began to see that she was not yet a free adult, not yet emancipated from her childhood conflict with her overly controlling and dominating parents. She was still trapped in her childhood pattern of hostile rebellion. Once this hostile pattern became apparent to her she saw that a way of life based on hostility would not be happy— that she was, in essence, destroying the very love and freedom she sought by misusing her sexual drive for an ulterior purpose of revenge. Linda was able, after a number of visits, to admit to feelings of emptiness and severe loneliness.

Parents desiring deeply their children's success in any form of endeavor usually have no conscious intention of using the children as pawns for their own dreams; usually they sincerely love their children and wish them happiness as they see it. As a result, the children usually have a basically sincere feeling of love for them in return and no conscious wish to hurt them.

Therefore, the hostility arising in children against parental impositions and deprivations typically brings considerable guilt. The guilt, in turn, creates a need on the children's part for self-punishment. The resulting rebellious behavior then serves two needs: attack on the parents and punishment for themselves. The whole process is acted out quite unconsciously. In cases that are spotted early enough, the untangling process is fairly rapid and easy, especially when the love overbalances the hate. Often the child's intellectual insight into the punishing behavior reveals it as just a weapon, and not something that is a major personality component. With this knowledge there may come enough freedom to permit new growth and fresh patterns. But if the pattern is deep seated in the personality, a systematic type of psychodynamic therapy will probably be indicated.

Love appears to be vital to happiness, but hostility and happiness appear to be discordant and incompatible, except, perhaps, in the rare case of overcompensatory reaction to unconscious hostility (see Chapter 9) wherein the hostility may indirectly generate socially useful work and acts of good will. But here, too, the individual is in jeopardy. Even a small amount of hostility can be threatening. This is seen in well-meaning, well-intentioned people who repress their hostilities and attempt to lead loving, generous lives of achievement. Without doubt this repression is far better for society as a whole than the criminal and criminoid acting out of hostility, but the nature of hostility is such that completely successful repression is probably not possible. Thus the good do indirectly what the bad do directly (with apologies to Plato, who said "the good dream what the wicked do").

The return of what is repressed from consciousness is a general human phenomenon in which poetic justice operates with unerring precision, although often unfairly: we have noted that the punishment is regularly directed to the desire that is the source of the hostility. For example, Linda, the young girl just mentioned, did not explode openly at her parents. Instead, her underlying resentment came out indirectly in disorders of her social relations and sexual experiences, which were unwittingly used to hurt her parents, and which eventuated not only in a lonely and unhappy life for herself, but in apprehension by the police for prostitution and drug abuse. Thus she brought on herself a punishment of stricter control than that she rebelled against.

A corollary to this is that the guilt that arises in the individual is not solely derived from unconscious impulses that never come through into action. On the contrary, in most cases the guilt is for actual behavior even though the hostile meaning of this behavior is not known to the person himself. This guilt for unconscious and indirect although actual hostile behavior causes tendencies to self-punishment. The form taken by the self-punishment is, of course, not accidental but specifically determined. As we noted earlier, the punishment fits the source; that is, the punishment regularly strikes the very desire which, frustrated, generates the hostility.

David is a young man who was doted on and excessively indulged as an only child. He strives now for prestige, feels dissatisfied and enraged by his failure to gain all the esteem he desires, and out of envy hates others who achieve this. His punishment is in the form of defeating his own strivings, so that he goes down instead of up his ladder of success. Significantly enough, David reports having repeated dreams of climbing a cliff but slipping down into a mine shaft. Dreams are, as Freud said, the royal road to the unconscious. In the dream our true motivations are set forth, although in disguised form.

It was at once clear that David was a man who was defeating himself and, through anxieties about his health and work, ineluctably driving himself toward failure by a self-punishing mechanism.

What was the crime that brought about his sense of guilt? David was charming, well-educated, and, at least on the surface, upright and conscientious. It seemed, however, that he had always been what he described as "too attractive to women." As a young man, David had been engaged several times but had always managed to break off these entanglements on one pretext or another. Finally, with reluctance, he married a lovely girl. But almost from his wedding day he was disappointed and dissatisfied. Four children were born to the marriage and this only served to irritate him further. He resented helping around the house, refused to assume any authority over the children, detested playing with them, and wouldn't hear of spending time with them when they were off from school on holiday. In fact the only pleasure David seemed to enjoy during this period was a series of flirtations and affairs with a bevy of women. Toward none of them, however, did he form any sort of real attachment. In due course, however, he met a woman who was extremely well-to-do and it seems that her social position and wealth captivated him. He divorced his wife and married this new attration. While he was consciously aware that he did not love his new wife and that he never really loved his first wife very deeply, he placed all the blame upon them for his lack of happiness.

Superior as he was intellectually, David was completely unaware of the hostility in his life, which resulted chiefly from deep inner protest against any responsibilities and demands. He saw himself as considerate and thoughtful and never visualized the load of guilt and resentment he carried because of hating to give any love and responsible effort in a relationship.

During treatment the source of David's hostility was uncovered, bit by bit. His mother had been an extraordinarily beautiful and vain woman who had asked nothing from him, her only son, but praise and flattery. Preening herself in front of him in pretty new dresses and jewels, she rewarded his admiration with kisses and then left him to baby sitters and maids to entertain himself while she went out. She was not a malicious or mean woman, apparently, but simply a careless and childish one. As her son grew he began to dislike the emptiness of their relationship, but he repressed his hostility toward her and turned it inward on himself.

Because David had inherited her good looks and skillfully copied her charm, he was successful in attracting much more love and attention than he might otherwise have received. However, because of his inability to return love, he was not successful in keeping it. This, of course, increased his unconscious hostility, which in turn built up more guilt, and eventually demanded active punishment: real loss of his wife's love and feelings of responsibility toward him, the very deprivations in his childhood relationship with his mother that had caused the trouble in the first place.

Generally speaking, it is better for society and hence for humanity for hostility to be repressed, but this alone is obviously no final, enduring answer for the individual or the race. The return of the hostility, the resulting guilt, the motivations of self-punishment, comprise a major mechanism by which a childhood pattern comes into dynamic equilibrium and persists for life.

We have discussed the biopsychological nature of maternal love and the relationship of this nurturing care to the normal growth of the child to maturity. Let us now turn our attention to a wider field of view and note the implications for society of love considered in a spiritual and humane sense.

Science in the form of psychodynamics has come squarely face to face with humanity's great problems of good and evil, love and hate. Science can now discern the origins of these, that is, what shapes, influences, and determines them. It was in the nineteenth century that science began to come to some real understanding of these forces which, until then, had been almost solely the concern of religion. However, much misunderstanding has been generated about the attitudes of psychiatry toward religion because Freud's initial penetrations into the causes of emotional disorders concentrated on the importance of sexual motivations. He broadened the concept, as we have noted previously, far beyond sensuality, to cover love in its most sublimated forms and, in fact, practically all positive feelings between people. However, many ignored this and misunderstood the sum total of his views as carnal pansexualism. This, plus the vulgar misinterpretation of his descriptions of resolving repression as license to sensuality, resulted in a gross misconception of Freud and of psychoanalysis as antimoral, libertine, and anti-Christ.

The reality is precisely the opposite. In his personal life Freud was puritanically moral. So, too, for that matter were his scientific conclusions—namely, that the whole course of the libidinal development consists in outgrowing childish egocentricity and achieving the capacity for unselfish responsible love. This is the essence of his libido theory. Mental disorder, he said, is a matter of libidinal fixations that are caused by faulty upbringing during the earliest formative years; it is in essence the result of a failure to lose oneself sufficiently to be able to love another.

The striking point is that this conclusion, which has been amply confirmed by later analysts, is identical with that of the world's great religious leaders. Thus depth psychology, by a totally different route, came, millenia later, to the same "commandments" as Judeo-Christianity and other great religions have always held to: for a good life man must love fully and reduce hostility.

Yet on second thought this identity in the teachings of science and religion is not striking at all. For it signifies the confirmation, achieved through painstaking scientific work, of realities long divined and felt to be true by the mass of people. Moreover, with discoveries of the biological drive toward cooperation within animal societies, we can now say we have the beginnings of a scientific base for morality and ethics.

It is hardly necessary to state in detail how it is that dynamic psychiatry has reached this moral outcome, for all that has gone before in this book shows that the path from infantile egoism to relatively unselfish, responsible, and productive love is the path to emotional maturity. Put conversely, the failure to mature properly emotionally is the basic source of hostility and of deficient capacity to love. Excess of hate over love is a sign of emotional disorder, the result of warping in the emotional development.

In medical school the doctor learns that his task is to help make the bodily condition such that the curative powers of nature can heal most effectively. Thus the physician's power comes essentially from going along with nature. The role of the doctor evolved in society as part of man's adaptation to nature. The doctor is himself part of nature's process of healing and prevention. This is undoubtedly why for so long religious leaders were called "healers." The underlying truth is that health of both mind and body, that is, full psychosomatic health, depends upon the harmonious development and operation of all the motivations, and anyone who helps people to the fundamentally proper ways of life in keeping with the deeper motivations of nature is thereby helping people to mental, bodily, and spiritual health. It is not only foolish to think of science and religion as being at loggerheads, but it is fundamentally untrue. The doctor and the "healer" have the same goal: the well-being of man. In this sense psychiatry is an instrument of religious feeling, of man's efforts to comprehend the forces of nature and the goals of mature living and to find his place in the universe.

Moreover, if the feeling of relationship to divinity does consist in part at least of a sense of closeness to and realization of nature's power and wisdom, and particularly of the forces that motivate mature behavior, then many diverse phenomena between religion and science become more intelligible. There is nothing new or revolutionary in this psychiatric approach except the specific importance of the mature drives.

In clinical practice where psychodynamic treatment is successful, the development toward emotional maturity is unblocked and hence moves toward increasing energy, freedom, and enjoyment of the mature responsible, productive, and independent drives, and the ability to love is increased. This ability, this growth toward emotional maturity in compassion and understanding, seems properly designated as *spiritual* growth. And the sense and feeling of the mature motivations in relation to other persons and to the rest of nature seems to be one component at least of what we remark as spiritual and religious feeling.

Dostoevsky seems to have been a man who had a deeply spiritual quality and a truly religious sense that enabled him to express an unusual sensitivity to motivation, particularly to the mature forces within man. His hypersensitivity resulted in all likelihood from the anguish of his own severe personal emotional disorders. Doestoevsky's interest in hate and suffering and his fight against these were coupled with painful longings to love and be loved. Probably these stemmed largely from his father's cruelty toward him as a young boy. But it was not his neurotic problems that made possible his capacity for sustaining an intense interest in man and for producing his monumental contribution to literature. In his short story, "The Dream of a Ridiculous Man," he expressed the central issue of human experience simply and directly: "The chief thing is to love others like yourself, that's the great thing and that's everything; nothing else is wanted."

Thus religious feeling seems related to a depth of and closeness to maturity of motivation. First, it involves humility, that is, a consciousness of the self as one tiny expression of the forces of nature, which underlie the whole universe and operate inexorably in each of us. Secondly, it involves the ability to love. Both of these demand a freeing of the mind from exaggerated or otherwise disordered infantile motivations and both result in the freeing of the creative forces within man.

Anyone who tries honestly to understand himself and others must realize that his ego perceives the interplay of motivations within his own mind, welling up from his own body and reacted to in accordance with his own early conditioning and his present situation in life. Each person's ego then perceives (so far as it is possible) these interactions in the forms specific to himself. If we could devise a modified and vastly more effective electroencephalograph, we could tune in to the other person's brain and experience in our consciousness what he is experiencing in his. How humble this should make us—and how considerate.

Insofar as man's very survival depends on increasing knowledge that will diminish hate and increase love, science should welcome religion and certainly also education as allies in a world with few allies. It should make its rapprochment with religion and the need for cooperation open and public. Science can only describe; by itself it can accomplish little toward aiding humanity in achieving the great goal of love. Science must make its knowledge known to those who can utilize it for progress toward the goal of love—and for such utilization religion has long had the organization and a shared objective.

Chapter 11

SOME LEGAL CONSIDERATIONS

"Ladies and gentlemen of the jury, the question we face here today is not whether John Doe committed the crime, but whether John Doe can be held *legally responsible* for this act." This question may reflect the clever dodge of a skillful defense attorney or it may be an expression of considered and legitimate doubt as to an individual's culpability in the face of psychopathology. Regardless of the circumstances or sincerity motivating the inquiry, it points to a persistent problem in our courts of law.

From the larger perspective of general human concerns, criminal responsibility is, of course, only one aspect of the much larger problem of human personal responsibility. In part we are what we are because of our genes, our heredity. For this we cannot take much responsibility. In part we are shaped by our early environment, especially that from birth to age about six. This has strongly conditioned us to certain patterns of thinking, feeling, and behavior. Hence a stong case can be made to show that our psychic lives are almost entirely predetermined and, so to speak, lived for us. It can also be argued that our feeling of free will is only an illusion, a subjective sensation that gives us the feeling that we are making choices and decisions, while in actuality each choice and decision is predetermined by our makeup interacting with our environment. If this is true, then no one is really entirely responsible for his feeling, thinking, and behavior—neither the good man for being good, nor the vicious one for being cruel.

On the other hand, perhaps we do have at least some degree of free will, of personal responsibility. Certainly our lives, our society, our government, and our laws are based upon this assumption. If we argue that there is no responsibility for criminal or any other behavior then we have chaos. Of course the whole problem of personal responsibility is a critical one, but we cannot disrupt our entire system of government, law, and society because it contains unresolved problems and difficulties; improvements must be developed as replacements before the present protections of society are discarded.

Clearly the problem of responsibility for criminal acts is far from solved; but as an initial step we should strive at least for a clarification of the basic concepts of mental illness and its relationship to this problem. The majority opinion in *McDonald vs. United States*, in speaking to the question of "whether a stated mental disease 'caused' the person to commit a given unlawful act or 'produced' that act," made the point that the question ought to be whether mental disease or defect "substantially affects mental or emotional processes and substantially impairs behavior controls."

Criminal behavior*—murder, rape, assault, and the like—is not usually "caused" by mental disorder, as the term *cause* is generally used. The reasoning however tends to be: "He committed a criminal act; he is to some extent abnormal mentally; hence, this mental abnormality 'caused' the criminal act, either by intensifying the motivation for the act or by weakening judgment and controls." This reasoning, while convenient, is hopelessly simplistic and fallacious. In reality, what is central in every criminal act is a disorder of personality. This can find expression in a number of different forms, which vary from time to time in the same person, and from one individual to another.

As an example of how a personality disorder can be expressed in different ways in the same person, let us note the case of Jim. This young man of high social, intellectual, and, apparently, moral caliber reacted to mild teasing by an acquaintance by shooting and killing him. For at least a day Jim planned the murder, working out elaborate accounts for his whereabouts that he could later use for an alibi. All during the day and evening before the shooting he conversed with people who knew him intimately and others who knew him casually. In the course of the investigation following discovery of the murder, no one could recall having noticed the slightest abnormality in Jim. Later it was learned that twice in the previous three years he had had episodes of open psychoses, for each of which he had been committed to a mental hospital for periods of about three months. This murder appeared as an equivalent of the previous psychotic episodes. Apparently in each of these two prior instances there was a reaction of rage of such intensity that it so disrupted his mental state as to produce frank schizophenic symptoms, disorganizing the ego functions of perception, integration, and mature behavior. The third time it came through as direct hostility, murder, without any such disruption that could be discerned by others or by the young man himself.

If this description is correct, then we have progressed a step in detecting the causal chain, while realizing that in this context causality is better understood as a network than as a chain. Here strong feelings and motivational forces, pressing for action, come to expression in the act. Going a step further we must ask why the rage and hate were so strong or the forces of control so weak, or both, as to produce murder. The answer to this question lies in the particular individual's makeup, in his personality, the essential components of which are his emotional interrelations—his patterns, attitudes, and feelings toward other persons. Jim was hypersensitive and filled with unremitting rage, chiefly from abysmal feelings of inferiority, which, in turn, stemmed from abuse by his father and extreme overprotection by his mother. This rage was usually covered over and controlled, creating overkindness that was characterized by a certain inner tension. When sufficiently intensified, it either disrupted the usual mental processes, producing psychotic episodes, or else broke through as violence. Possibly one reason it could break through in such action was that in early childhood he was repeatedly given harsh physical punishments.

Thus the real pathology, the real mental disorder, consists of disturbed feelings toward others—and also toward self. As we have stressed throughout this book, the pathology is always a pattern of emotional reactions formed in childhood in response to how the child was treated by other human beings, chiefly by those responsible for the child or otherwise close and emotionally important to it. Of course, under powerful enough external pressures anyone, no matter how good his human relations since birth, can show untoward patterns of reaction. This is widespread in times of violence such as war. This is not the essence of behavior that is criminal, for that arises from within the personality under ordinary conditions. Criminal behavior is an *outcome* of personality disorder, it is not *caused* by neurosis or psychosis or other symptoms of syndromes; it is, like neurosis and psychosis, itself a form of disorder. Criminal behavior is but one type of symptom.

The desideratum is to cure all the sufferers from psychosomatic disturbances, from phobias and other forms of neurosis, from addictions, from criminal acting out, from every other type of psychopathological symptom. But this is impossible for at least two basic reasons. First, psychiatry is not like surgery—it can only help people to help themselves. If a person does not have a powerful and sustained drive to change, psychiatry cannot change him. Secondly, all of these conditions are for the most part lifelong personality disorders. Even if the individual has all the will in the world to change, it may be too late and he may not be curable. Even help for persons who desperately want it is slow and not successful in every case, as where the childhood warping was too early, severe, consistent, and prolonged. Usually the criminal type of behavior disorder is not curable and even if it were, there are not enough psychiatrists available. Nor can there ever possibly be enough psychiatrists for a treatment that involves reopening the development of personalities so warped so early in childhood as to eventuate in criminal behavior. To think that a few months or even years in a mental institution will produce any permanent cure in the vast majority of cases is unrealistic. Psychiatric treatment for such disorders, in any form available today, is ineffective, unreliable, and impracticable. Because sending recidivists back to jail does not help them or change their behavior does not mean that sending them to a psychiatrist or mental hospital will achieve the desired effect, although this is certainly a gesture in a more rational, humane direction.

What, then, can be done? Let us look first at our present system. The jails are full to overflowing, crime is increasing, and the extraordinarily high rate of recidivism tells any person willing to listen that something fundamental must be wrong. Perhaps the basic fallacy lies in the concept of punishment for wrongdoing. This notion permeates the thinking of our society, and yet the jails show more often than not that its effect on criminals is the opposite from the intent. Punishment and incarceration have long been questioned as the best ways, first, to protect society, and, second, to help the criminal. But while new approaches to the problem are sought, we must still strive to make the present system work as effectively and justly as possible. This requires as a basic minimum that we agree on the definitions of certain key terms. Without sharpness of definition, terminology can only lead to confusion in reasoning, in legal opinions, in charges to the jury, and in outcome. But such sharpness of definition seems impossible in regard to psychiatric terminology. Most of the terms are broad and loosely used. There is a marked lack of uniformity in definitions of diagnostic labels, and more often than not inadequate objective evidence is offered for the diagnosis.

The District of Columbia Court of Appeals (in *Carter vs. United States*) stated:

Unexplained medical labels—schizophrenia, paranoia, psychosis, neurosis, psychopathology—are not enough.

> Description and explanation of the origin, development
> and manifestations of the alleged disease are the chief
> functions of the expert witness . . . the material from which
> his opinion is fashioned and the reasoning by which he pro-
> gresses from his material to his conclusion . . . the explana-
> tion of the disease and its dynamics, that is, how it oc-
> curred, developed, and affected the mental and emotional
> processes of the defendant . . . not the mere expression of a
> conclusion. The ultimate inference . . . of cause and effect,
> are for the trier of the facts.

Eventual agreement as to definitions of terms rests upon a
sound base of understanding. This must include an understanding of the emotional forces behind the phenomenon that
the term is meant to describe. Understanding of these emotional
forces was initiated by psychoanalysis and is being contributed
to by modern dynamic psychiatry. The following presents a psychodynamic discussion of a number of terms that are commonly
used and misused in considerations of criminal behavior and its
relationship to the law.

Insanity, the key term in the plea of "not guilty by reason of
insanity," is generally considered in the field of psychiatry to be
a legal term, not a psychiatric one. Probably among psychiatrists there is general agreement that it designates a disturbed
condition of thinking, feeling, and behavior of such kind and
degree that the person is unable to manage his own life as a free
member of society and therefore must be committed—voluntarily or involuntarily—to a mental hospital.

The term *insanity*, which is used to describe such a state of
mind, has the same meaning to the psychiatrist as it does to the
general public, to whom an insane person is one who is "crazy,"
"out of his mind." The insane person is one whose behavior is so
remote from reason and reality that we cannot talk and communicate with him in an ordinary and reasonable fashion. This
usual meaning of insanity is termed by the psychiatrist *psychosis*.

Psychosis can be defined psychiatrically in a somewhat more
technical way, which would be consonant with the dynamic psy-

chiatrist's view of the mind and its operation. Psychosis is understood as partial or complete disruption of the functions of the ego. How a person lives, how he acts, how emotionally healthy or disordered he is depends, in the final analysis, upon the health or disorder of his ego. He may, for example, have strong sexual or hostile impulses from his id, but if his superego is strong in setting his standards, and his ego is strong in its powers of judgment, reason, control, and in its directing of thinking and behavior, then he may use these forces in a constructive way. If his superego reactions are too strong he may feel so guilty about these id impulses that he becomes depressed. If he is too dependent to live up to superego ideals of, say, masculine independence, he may feel inadequate, frightened of life, inferior, and therefore, through the fight-flight reaction, enraged. This hostility may cause great guilt, or it may, if repressed by the superego, cause psychosomatic symptoms. On the other hand, it may be denied and excused, as in cases of paranoid projection, wherein the individual suffers under the delusion that he is not hostile but that other persons are persecuting him. In this latter case, the person grossly distorts his perception of reality to fit his emotional needs. The ego function of perception is thus disordered. In summary, then, we see how under emotional pressures from the id and superego or both, and/or also from the outside world, the ego functions may be more or less disordered. When they are grossly deranged and especially when judgment, control, and sense of reality are distorted, the condition is described as psychosis.

It is clear that emotional forces, especially hostility, which is our primary concern and the most constant factor in psychopathology, can affect the ego in many ways, depending upon the balance of forces from id, superego, and environment. Psychosis is one of these ways, but it is one form only in the whole range of mental and emotional disorders.

In psychosis many or all of the functions grouped together as ego are severely impaired or distorted: (1) Consciousness may be impaired or entirely suspended, the person having no memory whatever of what took place during the psychotic episode. (2) Perception, internal and external, may be distorted in almost every imaginable way and to extreme degree. The person may believe that he has a disease or deformity, or that small creatures are crawling about under his skin. Or, his delusions may be about the external world, particularly about people, as in those of persecution, already mentioned. If guilt, a reaction of the superego, is of certain form and strength, or if hostility, from the id, is directed against the self, psychotic depression may occur. The sufferer may feel himself to be guilty of the most heinous sins and crimes, and worthy only of punishment and death, which he may try to inflict upon himself. Gross distortion of reality is familiar to the psychiatrist as illusions, delusions, hallucinations. The psychotic may not know the date, time, or place, or he may mistake these, in which case he would be described as being disoriented. (3) Memory, reason, judgment, and other powers of integration may be deranged. (4) Control may be weakened to any degree. (5) Capacity to relate to others with healthy and friendly feelings and identifications may be disordered or lost almost completely so that no communication with others is possible. Where id and superego forces are powerful enough relative to the ego, the ego functions may be totally disrupted and the person seems to us completely confused and incoherent.

The balance of forces in the personality varies greatly from one individual to another. A thoroughly healthy personality is not common—that is, a person with no overly strong antisocial forces in his id, with a superego that has been formed of loving childhood relations and identifications with his parents, and with a current life situation within the limits to which such a reasonable and mature person can adjust. It is also obvious that there are many pathological dynamics with even more numerous outcomes, and that the outcome in criminal behavior is very different from the outcome as psychosomatic symptoms, neurosis, or psychosis. Combinations of one or more of these outcomes do occur, but each element is recognizable as a distinct condition in itself.

A superego that permits or encourages criminal acting out is in that part a criminal superego. An ego that accepts and acts out hostile impulses that are unchecked by the superego is a criminal ego. It is disordered, but very differently so from an ego that is so deranged in its functions as to be psychotic. The mark of criminality, as we discussed in Chapter 7, is the ego's acceptance and acting out of hostile impulses that society considers antisocial, immoral, and criminal. This ego, unlike the psychotic ego, may be strong and effective in all of its functions, as in the case of an outstandingly successful criminal who fully accepts his criminality.

It is not uncommon to see persons with circumscribed psychotic areas in their egos that serve the criminal drives; common ones are hostility displaced to society and paranoid trends. The latter involve delusions of being threatened by certain persons or groups, justifying use of all the other unimpaired powers of the ego to attack them.

Criminality is a disorder. Psychosis is a disorder. Both may combine in a person in various ways and degrees. But they are two totally different and distinct disorders. The term *insanity* makes sense if used in its usual meaning of psychosis.

The term *mental health* is not easy to define since there is no one psychiatric definition that is universally agreed upon. Descriptively it is a state in which a person is in harmony internally with himself and externally with his environment; this includes, in Freud's phrase, the ability to love and to work. More dynamically—that is, more in terms of the emotional forces that shape personality—it is emotional maturity combined with adjustment. Adjustment means harmony with the self and the environment. This equilibrium is dynamic; for example, a person may not be satisfied with his skills or environment but he is satisfactorily adapted to his efforts to improve these. A regressed schizophrenic, for example, who is entirely helpless and dependent in a mental hospital, may reach a degree of adaptation on this level, that is, as a parasitic baby, but this is not a mature adjustment and is therefore not mental health.

Maturity and mental health have been tersely defined as the ability to enjoy working and loving in good balance with socially acceptable recreation. Maturity is the end result of the development of the fetus and baby from parasitic dependence upon the mother into an adult who would be able to meet the dependent needs of spouse and baby responsibly and lovingly. The baby needs care and love to survive; it is completely dependent and needy of love; as it reaches awareness it senses its smallness and weakness with consequent feelings of insecurity, anxiety, inferiority, and competitiveness.

The drives of the child's id are to grow and develop; but this is achieved healthfully only in a setting of good human relations in which parents keep good feelings between the child and themselves. The child then forms a superego out of love for and identification with the parent that is loving, understanding, and supporting. With good relations during early childhood, the child's ego is free to develop its own functions. If the environment remains suitable, we have a person with a well-functioning ego, impelled by mature drives from his id, with a superego that is approving and supporting and in harmony with the rest of the personality. The mature adult can meet the needs of his family and his society by being relatively independent, responsible, and giving of love and work.

Mental disorder is a broad term covering every deviation from mental health, that is, from maturity and adjustment. This disorder may be primarily internal, in which case the deviations arise from within the personality. Or, the disorder may be chiefly external or reactive, as when a mature person is subject to excessive environmental pressures (such as in time of war). Under great enough stress even the strongest personality may develop symptoms and break down.

Mental is itself a term of mixed meanings. It is sometimes used to refer only to the intellect, as in *mental retardation*. It is often employed, however, to mean psychotic, as, for example, when a person suffers from severe anxiety and he and his family want to be reassured that this is "nothing mental." But *mental* is also used very broadly to cover every manifestation of the life of the mind. In this connection *mind* means everything, conscious or unconscious, that it is possible to experience subjectively—thoughts, feelings. These are primarily interpersonal and intrapersonal. Mind comprises all the forces of id and superego as the ego tries to harmonize them with each other and with reality. Thus, we could not experience psychologically, mentally, subjectively, consciously, the manufacture of additional white cells for our blood when we have an infection—this is subpsychological and not an emotional force, that is, not a motivation for the behavior of the organism as a unit.

Mental defect is also a very broad and imprecise term carrying different meanings. It is sometimes employed to mean only an intellectual deficiency, such as retardation; or, less frequently, it refers to a specific deficiency, such as a reading disability. It is not usually applied to neurotic symptoms, say stage fright, for example. It is rarely used in psychiatry and cannot be considered a psychiatric term of any established meaning. As used popularly and legally it may mean any deviation from mental health, intellectual or motivational. Used in this way it is applicable to almost everyone, since, as we have said, few if any persons enjoy perfect mental health.

Mental disease is, in one sense, almost a contradiction in terms. The word *disease* is fixed as meaning a condition identical with or closely similar to what we know as organic disease, such as measles, cancer, heart disease, and the like. It is true that all the mental disorders do indeed have the characteristics of the physical diseases, but the connotation established by this association is apt to be grossly misleading. Everyone understands that the body can, in response to infection, generate malaise and fever. Probably few, however, think that, for example, mistreatment of a child can be internalized and lead to the formation of a harsh and rejecting superego. This, in turn, would generate in the id a reaction of hostility, which is projected and experienced by the child and later the adult as phobias. A person with pervasive inferiority feelings and under powerful pressure of hostility may be as allergic to slights as an asthmatic is to ragweed pollen.

The connotation of disease derived from physical conditions is also misleading in regard to treatment. In organic medicine we are accustomed to thinking of disease entities for which there is more or less specific treatment, medical or surgical. Psychologically, however, we deal with disorders in the development of the total personality, often from birth. Tranquillizers may mollify tension and anxiety, but unlike the antibiotics they do not touch the basic cause. This is a matter of insight whereby the road to emotional development is reopened. It is a matter of outgrowing old childhood patterns that have become inappropriate to adult living and forming new, more mature ones. In the overwhelming majority of cases there is a deep-seated chronic personality disorder behind the symptoms, so that quick results are usually temporary palliation and not removal of the cause. Perhaps in time drugs may be found which affect therapeutically some causal elements in certain emotional conditions as suggested by recent biochemical studies of psychotic depressions and schizophrenias.

The term *paranoia* is used to refer to a psychosis presenting delusions of persecution of a rather clearly defined type, well supported and defended by the individual. These systematized delusions generally involve a more or less circumscribed portion of the personality although they tend to spread out slowly, involving more and more. In this state of mind there may be no marked tendency toward deterioration, the illness having essentially a chronic course and often remaining unchanged for years.

Masochism is a term that has come to have the broad meaning of acting unconsciously in ways that are injurious, even destructive, to the self. What looks at first like an external force beyond control or like a natural error of judgment, may be seen to repeat itself in a person's life over and over and assume an unmistakable pattern of behavior. This self-injuring trend seems regularly to consist primarily of hostility taken out unknowingly upon the self although there may also be other mechanisms operating.

Guilt may be an intermediate step in masochistic behavior. For example, the individual may feel so guilty and deserving of punishment that he actually courts it, directly or subtly. Guilt comes most often from hostility, or at least it is most often closely associated with it. For example, if a man ruins his marriage and deeply hurts his wife by having extramarital affairs, it is not the sexual relationships that make him guilty, but rather it is the hostility and injury to his wife that gives rise to the guilt. Another mechanism is seen in the adult who was rejected as a child and feels that since his own parents did not value him he is certainly worthless and not deserving of success. Usually beneath this reaction is a burning resentment for the feelings of rejection, with or without much guilt. The fact is that intense hostility is apt to rebound, injurying the self as well as others.

Self-injury can take any number of forms—making a bad marriage, subtly wrecking a good marriage or promising career, antagonizing people, drinking, taking drugs, acting out criminally, ambitious striving beyond one's capacities, and every other way of self-defeat. Whether hostility is always taken out in some part on the self is not known. Perhaps there are completely criminal characters who were so mistreated and so trained in childhood that they can vent hostility upon others freely and without contrary conscience reactions. Such persons are generally considered to be monsters.

History abounds with examples of mass masochism, which are reminiscent of the lemmings stampeding into the sea to their own death: Athens and Sparta destroying each other, almost welcoming Roman conquest as a relief from intranational strife; the Hundred Years War; and after it the War of the Roses, that "indefatigable suicide" of the Anglo-Norman nobility. It is very hard, said Winston Churchill, to discern one's own self-interest or that of one's country. Not only, we may add, because of the intellectual difficulties of obtaining and interpreting facts and judging people, but also because of the internal emotional tendency to injure, even to destroy, one's self. This tendency is usually at bottom a reflection back upon the individual, directly or through guilt, of his own hostility to others.

Personality disorder is a broad term used in two ways, one of which has a clear-cut psychodynamic meaning. Descriptively, it is used in psychiatry as roughly equivalent to *character disorder* in contrast with the terms *neurosis* or *psychosis*. For example, a man is in all observable ways mature, loving, and responsible, but he is afraid to go higher up than the third floor of any building. He is said to have a normal, healthy personality, but to suffer from a neurosis—meaning in this connection a circumscribed area of difficulty, of psychopathology. Dynamically it may turn out that he had a harsh father and therefore has a harsh part of his superego, which renders him particularly sensitive to all forms of authority. This may then create an underlying rebellious rage that is well controlled by the otherwise healthy ego and superego, coming out only as the phobia. Psychodynamically, *personality disorder* refers to the underlying disorder, however circumscribed it may be in the development of the personality. In this example it would be the harsh superego with its inner conflict and the hypersensitivity and rebellious rage toward all authority. In this sense, every type of mental and emotional symptom (excluding organic and purely intellectual impairments) is a manifestation of some degree of personality disorder.

Character disorder is a form of personality disorder in which what is usually and vaguely called a "good character" is deficient; that is, the individual fails to live up to the generally accepted standards of responsibility, honesty, loyalty, and the like. Often he is too dominated by desires for immediate pleasure to be fully reliable and responsible. The broader term *personality disorder* seems to be replacing *character disorder.*

Personality means, psychodynamically, the makeup of a person's id, superego, and ego, and their accustomed ways of functioning, internally with each other and in relation to other persons and the total environment. Each individual's environment is in part happenstance and in part what he consciously and unconsciously makes it. The makeup and accustomed functioning of the personality is predominantly a result of the emotional patterns formed in early childhood. It is these early influences that are internalized as superego and which encourage or warp proper maturing of the id and of the ego.

Sociopath is a diagnostic term. It means an individual in whom the disorder of personality is not much repressed. In such a person, for example, hostility is not expressed in psychosomatic or neurotic symptoms; instead, the hostility and much of the childhood emotional pattern that generates it is acted out. If the hostility is strong and unrepressed the condition has criminal elements in it; if not, then the person is more of just a nuisance to others and usually also to himself. He may be regarded only as an eccentric. He may have a life pattern of an endless series of marriages and divorces, of making and losing money, of unconsciously getting himself discharged from jobs, and in a variety of other ways of acting out a disordered childhood pattern of human relations.

The term *sociopath* is used to designate the psychopathic personality, since the symptoms of psychopathy are manifested in the field of social behavior, rather than, for instance, in psychosomatic symptoms or neurotic ones. Thus *sociopathic personality disturbance* is used to refer to individuals who are ill primarily in terms of their failure or refusal to conform to social, cultural, and ethical standards. This group does not include those whose conduct and behavior is symptomatic of more primary personality disturbance. *Sociopath* or *psychopath* generally is used to refer to an individual who is not readily classifiable as intellectually defective, neurotic, or psychotic but whose behavior is characterized by what comes to be recognized as patterns of recurrently episodic impulsivity, irresponsibility, lack of emotional control, and inadequate or unstable educational, marital, occupational, and other social adaptations.

Abnormal mental condition is not a technical term but a general expression of the greatest breadth, which is used to cover any and all deviations from mental health. But, as is usually the case when the word *mental* is used, this term can also be used more narrowly to mean psychotic. Here too, then, a fear of heights would be an abnormal mental condition in the broad sense, but not in the narrow. *Abnormal* is itself to some extent a misleading term, for it implies that the normal, in the meaning of average or majority of people, is healthy and that the deviations from this normal, mental health are the exceptions, the abnormal. However, as discussed above, full mental health is rare. The abnormal, then, is in fact the condition that obtains among the great majority. Thus to be useful in a specific situation, as in a court of law, *abnormal mental condition* must be very sharply defined.

Some deviation from mental and emotional health and adjustment will be found in every defendant because it is (present in nearly every person (and therefore in the lawyers, judge, and every member of the jury). Their relationship to criminal acting out is also almost inevitable, since nearly everything a person does is the expression in action to some degree of most or all his motivations. It is particularly true that most of a person's psychopathological motivations (disordered childhood emotional patterns) enter into his pathological behavior. If a person commits a criminal act it would be rare for this not to be an expression of his psychopathology. Hence, it is a foregone conclusion that in every criminal case psychopathology will be found and this wil be related to the criminal behavior.

Schizophrenic reaction is one of the relatively few basic psychological ways of reacting to emotional stress. The schizophrenic withdraws emotionally from relations with other persons and becomes excessively preoccupied with his own fantasies. The feelings that produce the fantasies usually give them a bizarre quality, which also is evident in the individual's thinking and behavior. Many or most people have schizophrenic reactions of a very mild degree at times when, under certain kinds of stress, they react by withdrawing emotionally. If this type of withdrawal is strong in a person, it may be recognized as an important trend in his makeup. Such a person may, however, be productive and successful and able to maintain a good family life. He may be called *schizoid*—the most characteristic feature of this is, besides a certain bizarreness of thinking, the feeling that life lacks resonance and responsiveness. If the reaction is still stronger, it may be diagnosed as *ambulatory schizophrenia*. In the extreme the individual may withdraw so completely that he has little or no emotional contact with anyone, and his fantasies include distortions of reality such as illusions, delusions, and hallucinations. The person lives in a world of dreams, which he experiences as reality. In this extreme, he is psychotic. Such a state of schizophenia may be acute, episodic, self-limited, and sometimes brief; or it may be chronic and lifelong. So far as questions of insanity are concerned, the condition is significant only quantitatively, that is, only if it is so severe that the individual is psychotic.

Since criminal acting out is a form of behavior disorder, it is folly to think of treatment in the ordinary terms of medical practice, such as treatment for pneumonia. Rather it is a question of whether the condition is influencable at all and if so to what extent, and whether punishment by law would be an effective procedure as treatment, as a deterrent to the offender and others, and as a protection for society.

Thus Jim, the young man mentioned at the beginning of this chapter, was committed as permanently and incurably dangerous because his hostility had produced two psychotic episodes and then a murder. After two years the family requested that a new examination and evaluation of Jim be made in the hopes that he could be discharged into society. The problem in such a case becomes one of prognosis: Will Jim's experienc᷾ of the last two years in a hospital for the criminally insane prove an adequate and permanent deterrent to him? Or, will his personality disorder again generate enough hostility for some sort of episode and, if so, what form will it take? Will it disrupt his ego functions to produce psychosis, or, with these functions relatively intact, will it again break through nakedly as murder?

Certain of the problems in the present system of dealing with criminals are fundamental. For example, it is the essence of democracy that everyone be considered equal before the law. This, of course, precludes recognition of individual differences. However, if a man snatches a purse, no rational disposition can be made without knowing his major motivations for this, the relation of this act to his personality, to his accustomed feelings and behavior. Only with this knowledge can it be predicted with any confidence what his future behavior will be like and whether it will be influenced by punishment or other procedures.

At one extreme the purse-snatching may be an isolated reactive bit of behavior in response to unusual emotional strains. That such a combination of pressures will recur with this intensity is probably unlikely. Moreover, since the man's personality is mostly sound, he probably will not repeat the act. At the other extreme we have the confirmed purse-snatcher. His behavior in this respect is probably not influencable by punishment or by psychiatric treatment. In both of these examples the behavior is the result of emotional disorder but not of psychosis. In the first case there is no great need to protect society, but in the second there is. A third possibility is that the man is actually psychotic, perhaps schizophrenic. For practical and reasonable disposition it is essential to have a usable diagnosis in each individual case.

In regard to the emotional disorder, if a person commits an act in a florid, unmistakable psychotic state in which he has delusions and hallucinations, this is one situation. If the act is not committed in a psychotic state, then it is usually the result of an emotional disorder which, as we have stated, is a manifestation of a personality disorder. This arouses our sympathy for the man who commits the act, but that should not impair our primary obligation of protecting society. If a man has typhoid fever or smallpox, he has our full sympathy and should have the best medical treatment, but the doctor's first duty is to protect society by isolating the carrier of a contagion. For the protection of society it makes little difference whether criminals are thought of as bad or as sick.

Almost everyone has some form of personality disorder, but usually it emerges in psychosomatic, neurotic, or other symptoms and not in directly hostile, criminal acting out. To say that the criminal is not responsible for his acts because of how his childhood has shaped his personality is, for the most part, true; but this is true of *everyone*—none of us are completely and entirely responsible for how we are. All our personalities with their heterogeneous traits, have been shaped in large degree by our childhood emotional reactions to those who reared us and were close to us. We have all been helped or warped in our growth toward maturity. Nevertheless, the more mature and responsible people, who have better personal relations and are better socialized, must protect themselves against the more infantile, warped, and hostile personalities. This is the prime function of the justice system.

Chapter 12

HOSTILITY AND POLITICS

The population is a reservoir of conscious and unconscious hostility. Poised in counterbalance to this implicit threat to survival are morality and ethics. They are expressions of the mature forces of cooperation upon which society is based and without which life in community would be impossible. Demagogues rise to power chiefly by organizing and manipulating the latent hostility in the body politic. Hence they so often begin with little lies, twists of the truth, and other corruptions of morality and ethics, the dikes against the ever-present sea of hostility, seeking to make little cracks that will widen to let through the latent elements of violence and permit criminal and criminoid action to be expressed without undue hindrance. Our central concern here is not with specific political actions and beliefs but rather with the personal, emotional forces that influence and often determine an individual's political feelings.

The deepest sources of political attitudes lie in childhood. In general, adults repeat in their social and political experience the pattern of family government that they knew in childhood. More than twenty years ago Otto Klineberg did a fascinating survey, "Tensions Affecting International Understanding," for the Social Science Research Council. Among other findings Klineberg reported how authoritarian homes in Germany produced authoritarian (Nazi) adults, while antiauthoritarian homes produced democratic (anti-Nazi) adults. Many other sociological and anthropological studies have since sketched much the same pattern. Given the considerable amount of evidence that has been collected by researchers, we are safe in saying that democracy, as most of us consciously desire it to be, requires first and foremost the existence of basically democratic homes. This means homes wherein each member of the family has his individuality respected and his voice heard. It also means that leadership, not dictatorship, should come from those most worthy to lead. Neither tyranny by adults nor tyranny permitted children can lead to democracy in the family.

Looking more closely, there are four fundamental problems that must be met in the course of family development. These are: (1) the child's attractions to and rivalries with brothers and sisters (or, if an only child, with other children); (2) the child's attractions to and rivalries with parents; (3) the child's adaptation to its dependent position in the custody of adults; and (4) the child's adaptation to the parents' position of power over him. The potential tyranny in these last two problem areas has already been examined in Chapters 4 and 5. Let us, therefore, turn to a discussion of how political feelings may be affected by the adult's childhood experience of sibling rivalry and the parental relationship.

It is very likely that the child's emotional problem of adapting to brothers and sisters is the root of later needs for equality among grown men and women. Children demand equality of treatment from their parents, and this forms a foundation for the adult's desire for social, political, and economic equality. At the same time, the pathology of rivalry with brothers and sisters may provide the nucleus for pathology in an individual's later view of social equality. If one child is grossly favored over another, he may turn into a social being who expects, wishes, and demands that he himself or his small group be favored over other persons or other groups in society. Conversely, children who have been rejected often mature into adults who gravitate to the fringes of society, feeling that as they had not been accepted by their own parents they will not now be accepted socially. Many of them yearn for love and acceptance just as they did in childhood. Relentlessly they seek it, but inexorably following their childhood pattern, they never achieve it.

It is probably in the child's relationship to its parents that the hierarchical pattern for all societies has its roots. One reason why democracy has been so constantly threatened from without as well as from within may be because of the despotism that is still exerted within so many homes. Children who come from families in which this is not true will not accept such a society; they say with Abraham Lincoln, "I would be neither slave nor master."

The basic problem arising out of the parental relationship that has political implications has to do with the adult still aggressively seeking to gain the power that he wished to have as a child so he could be like his parents. Perhaps this is most clearly seen in the relationship of a boy to his father. To the small child the father appears big and powerful. Wishing to be like him, the small boy tries in many ways to be big and powerful also. If he develops well, if his parents understand and help him with this rivalry as with his sibling rivalry, he will solve these problems and eventually, as an adult, achieve a mature identification. But such childhood attitudes as dependence, submissiveness, and guilt, persisting strongly, make many adults feel anxious and weak. Consequently they struggle, as it were, to be the father in their relations with others. What they attempt to do is establish a predominant position for themselves with little regard for the realities and needs of other people. Unresolved relations to the father and the mother thus can become an important enemy of democracy and an aid to dictatorship and regimentation.

These family problems of childhood and the type of solution found by the child form one very important factor in the individual's later social and political reactions and motivations. But other childhood motivations also are of great importance, persisting as they do within the adult and shaping his views and behavior far more than his reason guesses.

If we look at an individual like Hitler we can see a very interesting example of the relationship between individual dynamics and group (in this case, national) dynamics. First let us sketch a few rough biographical details. He was born in Austria in a town near the German border in 1889, when his father was fifty-two and his mother twenty-nine. He had a half brother (seven years older) and a half sister (six years older), both of whom had been born to his father's second wife, who died of tuberculosis. The father's third wife, Klara (Adolph's mother), had been a maid in the inn where he and his second wife lived. She had probably been his mistress for a number of years and may in fact have been his niece. She was a devout Catholic, a meticulously clean housekeeper, and a woman of very little formal education.

Klara Hitler's first three children were born in rapid succession, and then all died of natural causes within weeks of the birth of the third. Adolph was born during the year following these deaths. In the face of the compound tragedy of having three children die within a year, Klara was doubtless exceedingly anxious over the possibility of losing her fourth child. Consequently, she was overprotective toward Adolph, who was sickly at birth. As Gertrud M. Kurth has noted,

> it seems quite likely that, in what may have been a kind of panicky tension, Klara handled the infant at the breast in a matter that transmitted to the baby a threat of being overwhelmed. . . . Clearly, such maternal behavior is bound to interfere with the development of the infant's and the toddler's ego functions, specifically with the development of individuation and autonomy. Concomitantly, the child's ability to develop viable and ego-syntonic identifications and durable object relations is severely undermined. In fact, it is legitimate to say that the mother who stunts her child's development by forcing him to remain a baby for too long virtually "kills" some of the child's indispensable functions.

Hitler's father was a chunky, authoritarian customs inspector. During Adolph's childhood and youth, the often brutal man was locked in an intense struggle with his son. The battle was waged over the father's constant attempts to assert his dominance over the boy. Young Adolph was, in part, tempted to yield and become submissive to his father, but in another part of his makeup he was panicked by this possibility and felt that his identity and integrity as a person would be swallowed up and destroyed if he yielded. The notion of submission was intolerable to him, and as a result he fought against it with all his psychic resources of defense. Typically, like every child, he saw only two possible outcomes: either submit and be destroyed psychologically, which was unthinkable, or else identify with the aggressor, that is, be the dominating one and thereby defend against being dominated. Most of this conflict raged within the boy unconsciously.

It is quite possible that Hitler's "hypothetical" cases of Viennese family life, which are described in *Mein Kampf*, are in fact barely camouflaged accounts of his own experiences. If this is indeed the case, and there is considerable evidence supporting this notion, then the passages in *Mein Kampf* offer us a revealing picture of Adolph Hitler's family life during childhood. Here is an interesting excerpt:

> So, from their earliest days, the young children become familiar with misery. But things end badly indeed when the man from the very start goes his own way and the wife, for the sake of her children, stands up against him. Quarreling and nagging set in, and in the same measure in which the husband becomes estranged from his wife, he becomes familiar with alcohol. Now he is drunk every Saturday, and in her instinct of self-preservation for herself and her children, the wife fights for the few pennies which she wangles from him, and frequently her sole opportunity is on his way from the factory to the saloon. When he finally comes home on Sunday or Monday night, drunk and brutal, but always without a last cent and penny, then God have mercy on the scenes which follow. I witnessed all of this personally in hundreds of scenes and at the beginning with disgust and

indignation; but later I began to grasp the tragic side and to understand the deeper reasons for their misery.

Again from *Mein Kampf* we have this revealing passage:

Now let us imagine the following: In a basement apartment of two stuffy rooms lives a worker's family of seven people. Among the five children there is a boy, let us say, of three. This is the age at which a child become conscious of his first impressions. In many intelligent people, traces of these early memories are found even in old age. The smallness and the over-crowding of the rooms do not create favorable conditions. Quarreling and nagging often arise because of this. In such circumstances people do not live with one another, but on top of one another. Every argument, even the most unimportant, which in a larger apartment would take care of itself for the reason that one could step aside, leads to a never-ending, disgusting quarrel. Among the children this does not usually matter; they often quarrel under such circumstances and forget completely and quickly. But when the parents fight almost daily, their brutality leaves nothing to the imagination; then the results of such visual education must slowly but inevitably become apparent in the little ones. Those who are not familiar with such conditions can hardly imagine the results, especially when the mutual differences express themselves in the form of brutal attacks on the part of the father towards the mother or to assaults due to drunkenness. The poor little boy, at the age of six, senses things which would make even a grown up person shudder.

When Adolph was eight years old the family moved to a new town, at least in part for the purpose of gaining better educational opportunities for the boy. Here the school was attached to a Benedictine monastery. Already we can see the young boy's fascination with the idea of domination. He was intrigued by the black-robed monks and particularly taken with the Abbot ruling over his flock with absolute authority. The church ritual and ecclesiastical music delighted him and he took singing lessons and joined the church choir. In *Mein Kampf* he says: "Again and again I enjoyed the best possibility of intoxicating myself with the solemn splendor of the dazzling festivals of the church." Later he wrote, "it seemed to me perfectly natural to regard the Abbot as the highest and most desirable ideal, just as my father regarded the village priest as his ideal." His fantasy life seemed to center around ways of joining the community of monks and eventually becoming the all-powerful Abbot. It is noteworthy that one of the abbots had his coat of arms displayed on the church and it prominently contained a swastika.

Adolph's conflicts with his father persisted and the boy more and more reacted to the threat of the older man's domination with fear, rage, and a drive to dominate others. By the time he was eleven, he had already developed many difficulties in social and academic adjustment. A teacher remembers the boy at twelve as "definitely gifted, but only in a one-sided way, for he was lacking in self-control, and to say the least he was regarded as argumentative, willful, arrogant, and bad-tempered, and he was notoriously incapable of submitting to school discipline." Adolph became interested in reading and constantly poured over military accounts, which he found in popular magazines, of the Franco-Prussian War of 1870-1871. He then discovered Karl May, who wrote fictional pieces about the "Redskins" of the American Wild West. These stories appeared every few months and featured as a hero Old Shatterhand, an American cowboy who specialized in slaughtering Indians. This grandiose hero justified this butchering by his own innate infallibility and by claims that the Redskins were an inferior race. When all the Redskins were done away with, Old Shatterhand moved to Persia and slaughtered Arabs. (It is interesting to note here that years later, when the Nazi armies invaded Russia, Hitler sometimes referred to the Russians as Redskins.)

When Adolph was thirteen years old his father died of a lung hemmorhage. He wrote in *Mein Kampf* that this event "plunged us all into the depths of despair." Although he became the male head of the family, there was little visible evidence of any permanent change in the boy. He continued to have difficulties at school and gained a reputation for baiting teachers and quarreling with students. Even though his father was now dead and thus the threat of domination removed, Adolph's pattern of response to that conflict with the older man persisted for it was by now a deeply ingrained feature of his personality.

By the time he was fifteen his teachers had apparently had enough of this troublesome boy and he was expelled from school. His mother then arranged for him to attend a school in another town and to live in a boarding house. Although his academic work was poor, he managed to receive a certificate that his work was completed. However, this did not entitle him to proceed to higher education. The following episode from his life during this period is a telling one. The night that he received his certificate he went out to celebrate, and after getting drunk he passed out on the road. A milkman woke him the next morning and he had a complete amnesia for the previous night. The certificate was gone and he had to apply for a copy. When he went to pick up the duplicate certificate the school principal called him in and showed him the original, which was torn into four pieces and covered with brown stains. Apparently he had used it as toilet paper when he had gotten drunk. Nothing could more clearly have expressed his total contempt for school and authority. Years later he wrote that he considered most teachers to be mad and poor influences on their pupils.

As is usually the case in conditioning experiences, the pattern of reaction established in childhood toward a parent spreads to other people and situations involving authority and power. Young Adolph's fear and rage in the face of the threatened domination by his father came to characterize all his later experiences. Interestingly enough, when Hitler went to Vienna for the first time he became intrigued with the social democratic party. When as a workman, however, he was informed that he *must* join a trades union (which was a socialist body), his positive disposition toward the party changed radically. The notion of being forced to do anything was abhorrent to him and he refused to join on those grounds alone. With ever-increasing violence he argued that he would under no circumstances yield to the demands of the socialists. Finally he was told that he must join the union or leave the job. If he refused both these alterna-

tives, he was assured of being thrown off the scaffolding. In
Mein Kampf he reports that he gave way to terrorism and left
his job.

Combined with this abhorrence of being dominated was, as
we have said, Hitler's powerful drive to dominate others. One
key aspect of Hitler's fascination with the past military glories of
Germany and the violent destruction of "inferior races," which
developed early and intensified during adulthood, was his fantasy of being stronger and more powerful than his hated father.
Hitler seems to have made a connection between his father and
Austria. He detested the Hapsburg monarchy that ruled Austria
and catered to such "inferior races" as the Czechs, Slavs, Bo-
hemians, and Hungarians. He longed for the day when Austria
could be reunited with Germany so the Austrians of Germanic
background would again be supreme rather than only another
minority group in Austria. Symbolically, Germany's triumph
over undeserving and inferior races probably represented his
own victory over his father.

It would also represent his own victory over himself, that is,
over the weak submissive part of himself that wanted to yield to
his father's domination. He hated this aspect of himself, this
weakness, and he detested anything or anyone that reminded
him of this. Many books have recently appeared detailing Hitler's personality and it seems likely that part of this weakness
may have consisted of his underlying over-attachment to his
mother and his failure to mature out of it. Since it is not our goal
to diagnose his precise dynamics, we will take no stand on this
issue other than to note that some of the resulting hostility that
grew out of his sense of weakness was directed against himself.
Hitler's masochism is clearly and dramatically revealed in his
orders to his generals near the end of the war to stand and fight
even in the face of certain disaster. Chronicles of the war report
how, for example, German soldiers were forced to die on the
near bank of a river when they could easily have retreated to the
other side, which could have been defended. But Hitler forbade
a retreat. To the very end, even when defeat was clearly in sight,
Hitler's orders were always to yield no ground but to fight to the
death, to the very last man. This entailed needless slaughter and

suffering. But for Hitler negotiation was unthinkable, just as it had never been possible for him as a child with his father.

In analyzing Hitler's character, Robert Payne has this to say:

> If he resembled anyone at all, it was Dostoevsky's ill-tempered "underground man," the man who comes out from under the floor boards, who "thirsts for power and is powerless, desires to torture and be tortured, to debase himself, and to debase others, to be proud and to humble himself." Like the underground man he could say: "The world can go to the devil so long as I have my cup of tea." He had no loyalties, no religious faith, no culture, no family ties. . . . His strength lay in the fact that he was totally alienated; it was all one to him whether he conquered the world or shot himself in the mouth. . . . What Hitler was committed to was his own rage, his own destructive fury. . . . He erupted like a force of nature, a tornado or a hurricane destroying everything in his path, and even now, though the evidence of his destructive fury lies all around us, it seems unbelievable a single man could cause such havoc. What he sought to do, what he very nearly succeeded in doing, was to dominate the entire world and reshape it according to his own desires, as though the world had been created for his pleasure. . . . There was madness in him almost from the beginning. His mind was a distorted mirror in which he saw himself as a vast imperial figure, overshadowing the world, the supreme judge and executioner, the destined master who had come to cleanse the world of its iniquities. His ferocious hatreds fed on mythologies, which he only half believed, and he had no deep affection for the Germans, who became the willing instruments of his self-serving will to power. In his dreams he saw himself as one marked by destiny, protected by a divine providence, but destiny and providence have their own mythologies. Because he lived, 40 million people died, most of them in agony, and as though this were not enough, he spent his last days giving orders for the destruction of Germany, devoutly hoping no German would be left alive to mourn over their

defeats. "They are not worthy of me," he said. Such was his ultimate verdict on the people who had obeyed him as blindly as the children obeyed the Pied Piper of Hamelin.

Probably the intensity of Hitler's conflict over domination/ submission and sadism/masochism contributed much to his genius for sensing power in politics. It was doubtless a large element in his spell-binding oratory, for he commanded response by the demonic power of his passions. To shed some light on this feature of Hitler's personality, we can look very briefly at the case of a young female patient who believed she had telepathic powers. Fact is, she was almost right. The woman was so keyed up by intense emotions that she could discern the faintest cues, which others would miss. Her ego could barely control her feelings and she was constantly in a hypersensitive state. The emotional intensity, threatening her ego with breakdown, kept her hyperacute and thrust at the very extreme of intuitiveness. In like manner, Hitler was keyed to the highest pitch short of emotional collapse. He could just barely restrain his egoistic drives to dominate and control others. The intensity of his own feelings, conveyed through his skilled, demogogic speeches, evoked a resonance in all those with similar emotional dynamics in their makeup. These people, of course, developed their dynamics just as Hitler did—that is, by the way they were treated by their mothers and fathers.

Here the question suggests itself: What are the relationships between national characteristics, such as authoritarianism, and child-rearing practices and family life? Further: What are the relationships between social and economic conditions and an individual's psychological orientation and response to experience? As Erik Erikson pointed out in *Childhood and Society*, child-rearing practices, that is, the specific ways in which members of the family interact and satisfy (or thwart) instinctual needs, are at once an expression of and a determinant of the behavior and personality traits of the individual members of the society and of the character of the culture. The way people behave and the character of their culture arises out of the way they adapt to specific situations. Thus it is always a matter of the personalities of the leader and his followers, including the national and racial traditions and ideals that are a part of their makeup, interacting with the current, external situations and pressures. Hitler at the time of Frederick the Great might have had few followers. But the German trauma of defeat following 1918 created a special set of circumstances. Gertrud M. Kurth believes that the enormous deprivations that the Germans had to endure during and immediately following World War I played an essential role in the people's compliance with Hitler's wishes and demands.

> The shortage of supplies vital for survival—food, fuel, and the like—was severe enough to cause extensive suffering and regressive anxiety. Moreover, the Inflation of the early 1920s and the Depression of the early 1930s, entailing unemployment and poverty, brought the additional shortage of emotional supplies such as self-esteem and self-confidence. In other words, it was this unique combination of economic and social crises that made it possible for Hitler to activate in the German people the same unconscious conflicts as motivated him.

When Hitler was asked how he could possibly put such a program as he envisioned into effect he replied: No problem—the kind of men we want will flock to us from all over Europe.

As one single example, the story of the destructiveness and ultimate self-destruction of Adolph Hitler and Nazi Germany provides a vivid illustration, and caution, that politics and political feeling cannot be considered apart from the larger concerns of psychodynamics. Politics serves as an expression not only of an individual's immediate estimate of what he wants for his own welfare, but also of his entire personality makeup. What a person wants for himself, how strongly he wants it, how much he considers the well-being of others, whether or not he would actually sacrifice others for his own goals, how far he will go with his hostilities to achieve his ends, how clearly he sees that his own well-being is intimately tied to his society's well-being—all these factors depend upon the kind of person he is. And this, of course, results from his childhood emotional constellation. There is a dynamics of political feeling that reflects the dynamics of the personality.

Sometimes political feelings result from very specific relationships to parents and siblings while in other cases they are derived from more general emotional dynamics. In either instance, of course, we are discussing only the personal, that is idiosyncratic, element in political feelings and not the normal and expectable reactions to real pressure, frustration, and injustice in society.

As an example of political feelings arising from a specific relationship in the family, let us look at the case of two brothers, Ted and Bill. The boys had a colorless, submissive mother and a strict, dominating father whose word was law in the household. As a child Ted, who was two years older than his brother, found that his best modus vivendi with his father was an unquestioning obedience, which obviated all conflict with the man. As an adult Ted fully accepted his father's unbending religious orthodoxy, his authoritarian political views and party affiliation, his rigid conventionality. What rebellion he had against the paternal molding was so effectively repressed that no signs of it were discernible. Politically then, Ted became the completely obedient follower, a dupe for the demagogue and the power hungry. Here was a man conditioned to regimentation, afraid of equality or democratic expression.

Not so the younger brother. Bill conformed, but only outwardly. A little beneath the surface seethed his rebellion until, just after adolescence, it finally emerged with tremendous power. He left home and swung to the opposite of his father on all major issues. He defied convention with drinking and sexual excess, turned openly against the father's church, and jumped all the way to the opposite side of the political fence, joining noisy protest groups where he could speak and act out his revolt.

Here, then, are two sons of the same family who develop political feelings and identifications that are extreme opposites. But in both boys there are underlying personality factors that are reactions to the same parent. Why these reactions assume different forms is a matter of the specific quantitative differences in all the emotional influences on each of the brothers. In this case the younger brother received enough support from his mother to enable him to rebel.

Another example of a specific relationship contributing to political feelings is that of Nancy, a young girl whose mother was one of those forceful widows who take hold of a business on her husband's death and drive on to outstanding financial success, while continuing at the same time to dominate her family. Neglected by her mother, and even resented by her as an interference with her career, Nancy was entrusted to a martinet of a governess, who did not hesitate to beat the little girl into submission. Probably only a good relationship to a younger brother as a fellow sufferer saved Nancy from a psychotic breakdown as an adult. As it was, when she grew up she spread her feelings of hostility against her mother to include all wealthy people and all successful business people. Politically she b·came what her mother's friends called "a traitor to her class." Various attempts were made by Nancy's family to blame her seditious political attitudes on the girl's so-called leftist teachers and the radical students whom she had befriended in college. However, external elements actually played a very minor role indeed in her particular political activities. On the contrary, these had to do with the hostility arising out of the specific emotional relationship with her mother. It was her hostility and rebellion toward her mother that led her to identify with radicals in college, and not vice versa.

In contrast to the situation with Nancy, we sometimes see individuals in whom external events play a rather strong role in evoking repressions and regressions that otherwise might be outlived. So it was with Hugh. He sought help allegedly because of stomach trouble and sleeplessness. He was a young man of high ideals who entered politics in an effort to break a corrupt machine. The fight involved many men who had little interest in the good of their party, and less, or none, in the welfare of the constituency. Hugh found that to accomplish anything at all he had to work and cooperate with many a criminoid character. He was infuriated by them to the point of losing his appetite for food and sleep. He was mature enough to have a true interest in others, but not mature enough or secure enough in his own identity or sense of independence to stand alone and to use all he learned for socially constructive ends. Too indulged in his own childhood, Hugh had tendencies to be criminoid himself, that is, to act for his own advantage regardless of others. If his associates had themselves been mature and working primarily for the public good, he probably would have identified with them, taken them as models, and gradually grown to that stature. Since they were as corrupt as they were, he was torn between his childish reward-seeking pattern and his avowed mature drives toward the good of others.

In all the vignettes sketched above, political feelings arose, as we have said, out of specific emotional relationships within the family. In the following case we look at an example of political feelings deriving from more general emotional dynamics. Glen, a recently married young man, has just embarked upon his career. He is a kindly person with good feelings for all people, well almost all. He shows one streak of prejudice, which is directed against those who are less fortunate than himself. In analysis it soon appears that Glen represses and is quite unconscious of an envy of those who have more money and more elaborate homes than he. His feelings are quite unreasonable because he cannot expect at his age the income of those who are much older. However, the infantile motivations do not respect such realities of time. The child wants what it wants at the moment it wants it. Glen is not even vaguely conscious of his hostility, born of envy, toward the older men who are his benefactors; he acts in a friendly way toward his superiors at work because he likes them and they like him and he is grateful for their attention and help. Also he fears they might otherwise fire him or in some other way damage his career. Meanwhile, he projects his hostility onto those who are less well off than he.

In them he sees the envious competition which he dares not face in himself, and he fears that they will take away what he has, although it is actually he who wishes to take from those who have more than himself. It does not occur to him that in reality he is closer to the young men in his firm than to his seniors. In a parallel pattern his political feelings develop: he distrusts the poor, the foreign, the have-nots, and the underdogs, and casts his arguments and votes only to aid the successful to be more successful. He represses his envious hostility toward the haves and identifies with them, turning his hostility on the have-nots.

A similar mechanism is encountered in some self-made men. One who came originally for advice about his daughter showed a typical pattern. Although this man wore tailor-made suits, although a chauffeur waited outside for him, although his honors were many and distinguished, he saw himself in his mind's eye as still a poverty-stricken immigrant laborer slaving at a menial job. His envy of those successful people who were now his friends was as intense and competitive as it had been when he was at the bottom of the ladder. But of none of this was he really aware; he repressed it out of shame and guilt. The hostility thus engendered found its outlet only against those who reminded him of his one-time inferiority—the poor and needy—and of the things he could not stand in himself. This is not the pattern of all self-made men. To be sure, many are especially understanding toward those who started with them but did not rise so far.

A somewhat different mechanism was seen in a man who was the middle child of a large family. Ross felt he had to compete for any love and attention he might get. Feeling deprived and unwanted he therefore felt an inferiority which he masked with a great show of amiability. As a businessman Ross continued to strive unremittingly for love, prestige, and a feeling of belonging, changing his views and attitudes to suit his associates. Inevitably this pattern was reflected in his politics. While Ross was a struggling apartment dweller in the city he identified with the underdog, but when he moved to a fashionable suburb he unhesitatingly switched his identification and affiliations in efforts to find acceptance (real or imagined) with his neighbors.

Here are two complementary examples of other outcomes of domination in childhood. Larry was a brilliant but unfulfilled man who had grown up an only child, much dominated by his mother and the many women in the family. He recalled several times how, when his grandmother wanted his grandfather to do something and the grandfather did not immediately comply but said he would do it later, the old woman would give him a terrible tongue-lashing. In response Larry always felt that he must comply and repress all rebellion against his grandmother and his equally strong-willed mother. He thus lived in constant guilt and fear, and, as a defense, developed an exaggerated need to be very good and very obedient in order to assure himself of his mother's love and avoid punishment by her. So great was this need that he could not bear any violence, even in a motion picture.

When Larry came for help, he was oppressed by a feeling that he must work all the time. He was unable to take even a single day off, not because of a great interest in his work, but because of his anxiety and sense of obligation. Often he felt as though his mother was standing over him telling him that he must work, work, work. Even the wishes of his wife for a vacation could not help him chase this ghost, this imago. Because of the passivity of Larry's behavior in areas other than his work, he was in no way active politically except in his dreams. In this arena he often projected the power conflict onto the political scene and identified and sympathized with the downtrodden, whom he saw as himself in childhood seeking freedom from oppression.

An almost opposite case was that of Ralph, a man whose effort to solve the same problem was made by identifying with the oppressor. He projected his mother's domination onto those who were in political power and identified with them. His own submissiveness was projected onto the underdog, whom he felt he must conquer as he himself had been conquered. Ralph feared that if he did not have complete control others might try to run his life just as his mother had done. In other words, he saw the world as he did in childhood—either dominate or be dominated. Ralph dared not cease to dominate lest he become the one who was dominated. This is typical. Most people see the world in the narrow restricted confines of their childhood relations to parents or sibling, in which they had to be on one side or the other.

These examples are meant to illustrate how underlying dynamics of personality can influence or even determine a person's political feelings and attitudes. No attempt has been made to survey the various specific and general emotional mechanisms. Our attention has been confined to political *feelings*, to the im-

portance of the emotional factors involved with no reference to
any actual facts of political life. Of course not all political feelings are entirely emotional; indeed it would be folly to deny the
rational and realistic elements in political attitudes. At the same
time, however, we must acknowledge, and this is the point of
this discussion, that most political feelings do have substantial
unconscious "rationalized" emotional components.

Projection, that is, denying motivations in oneself by attributing them to others, is counteracted in the mature individual by
the sense of reality and even in the immature person by experience and knowledge. Groups and nations are hard to know realistically and thus there is little corrective for immature, emotionally dictated attitudes. Therefore, as we have noted previously, many can imagine a foreign nation or an unknown or
simply unfamiliar group as having all sorts of strange characteristics and motives, with little appreciation of the members as
actual persons.

In the following clinical example the projected hostility was
directed not to another human being or group, but to a fixed
stereotyped notion of an animal. Bob, a man with very high
standards, had a terrible quarrel with his wife one evening. He
retired and dreamed that two snakes were whirling around together. Then one of the snakes came toward the dreamer, who
tried to step on it but did so in a clumsy fashion. After telling
this dream, Bob went on to say that snakes were dangerous,
venomous, and deadly, and that one must be sure to destroy
them. He was certain that the snakes in the dream represented
his anger of the night before, concerning which he felt much
shame and guilt. Bob thought that it was awful to fight this way
with his wife and that some of the things that he attempted to
say to her, but fortunately did not, were really vicious. In regard
to his clumsiness in stepping on the snake in the dream, he
thought of his difficulty in actually doing anything like that in
reality.

These few associations will suffice to illustrate the central
mechanism of the dream. Bob goes to bed distressed and critical
of himself because of the fight with his wife. In the dream he
handles this sleep-disturbing stimulus by saying, "No, it is not

my wife and myself fighting, it is only two snakes. It is not *my* impulses or *hers* that are dangerous, venomous, deadly, and vicious, it is snakes that are that way." But part of Bob's hostility projected onto the snakes comes toward him, and he seeks to defend himself by stepping on it. Thus by projecting his own vicious impulses onto the snakes, he justifies his hostility to t.1em and his impulse to destroy them.

Obviously his prejudice against snakes is shared by many people. The fact is that most snakes are friends of man. Most species are easily domesticated; in fact, some people who know snakes even keep them as pets. Further, they perform critical functions in the ecological balance of the environment. All this shows how unrealistic the idea is that all snakes are deadly and must be destroyed. This is a stereotype not unlike the ones formed and maintained about alien and minority groups. These prejudices also arise through illusions and projections that obfuscate reality, making it difficult to discriminate between what is and what is not really dangerous.

Here is another example of how hostility and projection are intimately tied to feelings of prejudice. Jane is a not unattractive spinster who was very strictly raised in a puritanical home. Now, at age forty, Jane is approached by a rather glamorous man who is doubtless intrigued by her very substantial bank account. He sets about to seduce her and with little difficulty succeeds. They begin a flamboyant sexual affair. At the outset Jane dreams of herself as covered with dirt. However, she manages to repress her guilt, shame, and self-reproach. According to the standards by which she was raised, Jane actually has reasonable cause to feel she is doing something dirty.

Before long, this feeling of dirtiness is projected in her dreams onto other persons. Now it is no longer she but rather others who are dirty. These others appear in her dreams as members of minority groups and soon this comes out as open prejudice in her conscious life. She develops an intense hatred of almost all minority groups because of her recently developed notion that they are dirty. Clearly, Jane is deeply enraged at herself for behaving in a way that so overtly contradicts her conscience, but all this hostility is turned outward onto others in the form of prejudice against members of minority groups.

From the foregoing it seems obvious that prejudice is not simply an artifact of our social or political organization. It is a deepseated psychological phenomenon that is rooted in childhood and persists neurotically, psychotically, and criminally when normal development to emotional maturity is warped. Prejudice is a symptom based on the dynamics of egotism, pride, status, and the needs to be loved and valued. In addition to these narcissistic components of the personality, fear and insecurity also give rise to feelings and attitudes of prejudice. Essentially whatever generates hostility in children is a potential source of prejudice.

In the political sphere feelings of prejudice may take the form of emotional leftism or rightism. Clinical observation reveals the dynamics to be as follows. The emotional rightist projects his feelings of inferiority and his hostilities upon the underdog. Hence he sees the underdog as representing that which he denies in himself. The underdog, therefore, represents to the emotional rightist all that is to be rejected, despised, and feared. The emotional leftist, on the other hand, through his own feelings of inferiority, identifies with the underdog, and projects his egotism, needs for power, and hostility onto the top dog. Thus the top dog, with whom he does not identify, tends to represent the rejected impulses within himself. While he envies the top dog, he also feels oppressed by him and therefore directs his hostility toward him. The childhood pattern is usually not far to seek.

These closely related but antithetical mechanisms are represented in two typical dream characters. In emotional rightists the dream figures, which of course differ widely in details, all seem to show the same basic mechanism. Here is one such dream: A poor old creature is working hard and has with him a poorly paid underdog assistant who is of little help. The rightist's associations with these figures have to do with his efforts to identify with those who have wealth, fame, and prestige. The dreamer goes in for large, expensive automobiles, and he generally looks down upon those who are poor and belong to minority groups. It soon appears from his associations, however, that he fights off a tendency to identify with the underdogs whom he represents in his dreams. He actually feels inferior to those with wealth, power, and position but denies this to himself in his efforts to feel that he is one of them. In so doing the rightist projects his inferiority feelings upon the less fortunate and the minorities and feels that they want to take away what he has. He also thinks that they are envious and hostile toward him, which may well be true. But by this projection he denies his own envy and hostility toward those who seem to him to have more wealth and prestige than himself. In addition, he asserts his superiority, power, and hostility toward those he sees as being beneath him. Since childhood this man, an emotional rightist, has always been fearsome and angry lest others get something more or better than he. Although well situated, he fears he will become the poor old downtrodden creature of the dream.

The opposite mechanism is that of the emotional leftist. In his dreams he is only a menial assistant working hard and getting little in return while an older figure is sitting back doing nothing but being waited upon. Often the older man is in the process of enjoying a sumptuous meal. Here the dreamer attributes to the older man all the gratifications that he himself wants while his own lot is seen as that of the menial assistant who works basely for the older man and is exploited by him. The leftist denies his own wishes for power, prestige, wealth, and self-indulgence at the expense of others and projects these desires onto the older man; he also projects his hostilities onto the older man and feels abused, depreciated, and taken advantage of by him.

The ideal situation is for each individual to be so mature that he understands his own motivations and those of others realistically and has humanitarian feeling not only for himself and his family, but for all people. Only in this way would he be relatively freed from projections and stereotypes. This is the emotional essence of democracy, as it is of Judeo-Christian morality. The psychodynamic mechanisms involved in determining the direction and form of political-emotional feelings are of great significance. But the basic problem is the hostility, the symptom of psychopathology, the force that warps the grasp of reality, impairs identification and fellow feeling, and prevents the shaping of societies without mass cruelty and destruction.

Part Five

TOWARD PREVENTION
AND CURE

Chapter 13

HOSTILITY BEGINS AT HOME

Every individual is motivated simultaneously by two sets of forces operating, as it were, on two levels: the conscious and reasonable, and the unconscious and irrational. The conscious and reasonable forces are in general the more mature; the irrational forces are essentially residues of childish reactions which, disturbed in development, furnish the source for neuroses, psychoses, illness, crime, and war. Mature love can be counted among the rational needs and drives of man. Hostility cannot.

Throughout this book we have stressed the point that of itself hostility is not a disorder or a disease. It is part of a basic biological adaptive mechanism—to meet threats, irritations, and frustrations by withdrawing from them or by destroying them. However, when hostility is generated from persisting childhood frustrations and misused for immature goals and resorted to in place of mature understanding and cooperation, it becomes a disordered adaptive mechanism, which is transmitted by contact from parents to children, from generation to generation, and is preventable only by cutting through this process of transmission.

This presents a great challenge to the family and, by extension to society. Ideally, the best approach is to reduce or eliminate hostility immediately in all parents. Unfortunately, since parents are, after all, only adults who were once children (and we all remain much the children we once were) this is impossible to achieve in any one generation. To be realistic and practical we must settle for the slower pathway of diminishing hostility as much as possible, sublimating the rest, and striving constantly to replace hatred and anger with responsible love and kindness. This is the same as the therapeutic process in the individual, where successful treatment means getting the patient securely on the way to improvement and development.

In this chapter we will deal with those aspects of hostile behavior that most often occur in the child-parent relationship. Then, in the following chapter, we will take a look at the problem of reducing hostility in the adult personality.

A key word to good upbringing is *balance*. An excess of attention may be as bad as too little. Too great a demand for growth is as unhealthy as too much babying. The child must be allowed, perhaps encouraged gently, but certainly not forced, to grow up into a mature interdependent adult. He must be accepted and respected as an individual who is a member of a group. Emotional development unfolds from infancy to form the mature patterns of parental and social adaptation. Disturbances in the main lines of development which, as we have seen, are the chief sources of hostility are: (1) persistent and excessive childish dependence; (2) insatiable needs to be loved; (3) extreme demands for prestige motivated by envy and rivalry; (4) a disordered conscience; and, generally, (5) revenge for misguided treatment during childhood.

It is always difficult to give practical advice about emotional problems, especially because they assume a unique form in each person. If it were possible to prescribe for the emotions in the same "miracle drug" fashion that we do for the purely physiological ills, we might lump together the following into one anti-dote for hostility: mature parental love, in which we include understanding and respect for the child's personality. We will amplify what is meant with some general suggestions, expressed as pragmatically as possible, about dealing with disturbances of each of these lines of development.

The growth of human beings, as of other animals, from conception to maturity, consists very largely in outgrowing dependence upon parents. The mature adult not only can be independent but must be interdependent. If parents overprotect the child, they impede its growth to self-reliance. If they force the child prematurely into independence, they may cause an aversion to it. Interference with this development produces an adult who, however powerful physically and intellectually, feels like a child, still craving the protection that he never outgrew. The underlying need to be dependent usually is in sharp conflict with the desire to be mature, causing an inner sense of insecurity and a reaction of impotent rage. The individual may try to overcompensate through a lust for power. Often these emotional dynamics eventuate in open criminality, even murder. No stable personal relationship or stable society is possible in which individuals who are apparently adult have not sufficiently outgrown their childish dependence.

During the earliest years of life almost total dependence is normal, to be expected, and should not be discouraged. In fact, because of other needs, it is generally felt that some of what used to be called spoiling is healthy during this period. This does not mean, however, that all infantile crying demands should be permitted or rewarded once a child begins to talk, or that the walking child should be kept so close to home and mother that no feelers are put out toward relationships outside the home.

When the child begins school his independent relationships with the outside world begin. How well he adapts to his larger social world will be reflective of how well he has adapted to family-group life. Trouble signs at this age—including overdependence—should be carefully weighed and the comments of teachers and doctors on how this behavior appears to objective, perhaps even critical, eyes should be considered and guidance sought on where the child may need help. Children who are repeatedly "bad" at this age obviously need help, but overly "good" children may also. The quiet, overshy child is often warmly welcomed and admired by his overworked teacher, but excessive compliance may signal lack of outgoingness and potential future difficulties.

In cases of flagrant misbehavior experts should be consulted. There are many excellent child guidance clinics throughout the country which can save the well-intentioned parent from much grief later on. Just a few hours of assistance may be all that is necessary at this age to help the parents understand the problem and set them and their child on the right track toward dealing with it.

The child's independence of his family grows in small ways. His physical skills demand encouragement; but the mother whose fear inhibits bicycle riding or tree climbing is no worse a handicap to the child's independence than the demanding father who flings his child into the lake with the cry of "Sink or swim!" Balance between protectiveness and prodding is needed here, just as it is in the child's expanding social life, his maturing emotional life.

With the early teens comes another stock-taking period as once more the child's growing independence—as against the lack of it—prepares the individual for maturity. In this ten-to-thirteen period the child begins showing natural signals of the breakaway that will eventually lead him to the outside world. Because these signals are more gently and quietly expressed than they are apt to be during full adolescence, parents can more readily overlook or shy away from them. But the way in which criticism of the home, lack of responsibility, failures in affection, or regular lapses in following accepted mores are handled at this stage can be of definite help in stabilizing the child's later adolescent explorations of the ways of group life, his relationships with the opposite sex, and his sometimes reckless attempts at premature adulthood. Basically, though, the core of the child's personality pattern is formed, as we have reiterated, certainly by the time he is six. If this is healthy he will, in ordinary circumstances, have no serious problems in adolescence.

But, conversely, if his interpersonal relations during these very early years have not been good, problems had best be watched for.

Little real emotional conditioning can be accomplished by parents after the early years, but behavior patterns can still be guided and help obtained, when indicated, in correcting infantile patterns. The wise parent, seeking to avoid future hostility because of the carryover of excessive dependency, will avoid thwarting or overindulging either the early, very real dependency of the infant, and aid and assist the equally real strivings toward independence, the infantile kernels of which flower in the preteens and teens.

The young child's needs for love are necessarily intense, the parents' love being its only guarantee of food, care, and protection. With growth, however, there is an increasing capacity for the enjoyment of loving-giving, culminating at maturity. The child then shifts from the receiving end, loved as a baby, to being capable of giving as a parent does who puts out responsible love and meets a child's all but inexhaustible needs. This same ability to enjoy giving as a parent carries over from the emotional life to the individual's social and economic life.

Deprivation and overindulgence are two of the common errors of upbringing that disturb the normal development of the need for love. As has been said earlier, if the emotional diet in early childhood is too rich or too poor, then the appetite for love in later life is distorted. True love is a genuine interest in the child's well-being, for its own sake, as well as a respect for his emotional individuality. Spoiling, overattention, excessive demonstrativeness are almost as poor substitutes for this kind of love as is the lack of it. Too great a residue of infantile desires for love cannot be gratified in adult life and this forms a source of constant frustration leading to irritability, to a sense of hopelessness and depression, to all sorts of neurotic symptoms, including dangerous rage.

It sometimes seems quite difficult to welcome a child into this world with real warmth. He brings with him so many problems —financial worries, caretaking chores, housekeeping upheavals;

but the chief, most vital problem is the strain he puts on those areas of emotional immaturity in each parent and in the parents' relationship to each other. If we can face the fact, however, that the child himself is not to blame for this stress, but rather our own weaknesses, then we are setting our feet upon the right path. True love for a child can only come from those capable of loving-giving. Certainly every child should be a wanted child. The unwanted child is all but foredoomed.

There is probably no one without some capacity for mature love. The problem facing most of us is not total lack, but rather greater development of what we have. Self-control, consistent giving of oneself, patience, affection, understanding, respect— all these help to develop a mature ability to love a child *for himself*. The parent-child relationship is one in which it is true that the more you give, the more you get.

Consider the parent who is quite incapable of loving the infant, but who shies away from the independence of the brash thirteen-year-old. Love to be love must be as steady as the North Star, encompassing both the irksome two-o'clock feedings of the baby and the back-talk of the adolescent testing his powers. As Shakespeare put it: "Love is not love that alters when it alteration finds."

A third powerful source of irrational hostility is found in an inordinate desire for prestige. Self-love is, within normal limits, an expression of self-preservation. The very life of a small child depends upon its being highly valued by the parents. But for the adult parent, a genuine, unselfish interest in his child, in others, and in responsible, productive accomplishment should be more enjoyable than the egocentric satisfactions natural to the child. The child's self-centeredness persists to some extent within the mature adult, but the proportion is changed; no longer are rivalry, envy, and the desire for personal prestige major motivations.

The two most common errors in upbringing that cause excessive drives for prestige and rivalry are favoritism and rejection. If the child's needs for prestige are not properly handled, then his infantile values of success may persist throughout adult life and he may become the kind of man of whom Napoleon cynically said: "Men will go through Hell itself for a bit of ribbon." Again and again we can observe how little of the interest of an adult lies in the task at hand and how much it is devoted to using the situation for his vanity. If a child is made to feel that he is the lord of the household or if one parent sides with him consistently against the other, or if the parents expect him to fulfill their own ambitions, then the child is prone to be fixed in a power pattern and feel in adult life that he must be the best, the preferred one. His own status will be all that matters, and every person will be to him primarily a hated rival, or a means to prestige. On the other hand, the child who is rejected and not sufficiently valued is likely to carry throughout life a sense of inferiority, an injury to his self-regard. In vain efforts to overcome the debility, this child too will fail to outgrow egotism as a primary motivation. He is foredoomed to frustration and therefore rage and hate, for all competitors can never be vanquished; childish egotism can never be sated.

The projection of parental ambitions onto the child is a common source of drives for power and prestige in the adult. When a parent compels a child toward the kind of success he or she once dreamed of, this pressure in itself usually creates a source of hostility, as rebellion and protest, as hate of rivals, or from frustration of these ingrained compulsive strivings.

There is, to be sure, nothing at all wrong with healthy ambition, competition, and success, provided it is the reflection of self-reliant, responsible doing, producing, building. It is only when it is mistranslated into egotism, hostile personal rivalry, and a childish battle for personal status that it becomes dangerous. The distinction between the healthy and the pathological in this regard is difficult to make today. The welfare of a society depends upon how much its members contribute, but our current standards of material success are based in great part on how much the members can take out.

A fourth common source of irrational hostility is friction between the individual and his conscience. The conscience should be the internalized result of gradual, reasonable socialization, balancing individual desire with the good of others and of society as a whole. But how often is the adult conscience little more than the imago of a depriving or overprotecting or threatening parent whose attitudes and treatment (psychologically and physically) have created feelings that impair rather than help development.

Physically harsh treatment is rarely anything more than a parent's own fears and hostilities being vented upon the helpless. "I'll teach you to hit people," cries the parent in a white heat, hitting out at the child. But what a lesson in hostility this turns into! Teaching is accomplished best by example, not precept, and the example here is an enraged adult using physical violence to meet a difficult situation. This provides the child with a model problem-solving technique that he is quite sure to follow. It is pretty certain that if the child were properly reared, the occasions for severe punishment would not occur.

Emotionally harsh treatment is less obvious but equally or more destructive to personality. The inculcation of too high ideals in childhood dooms the adult to incessant, hopeless striving to achieve the unrealizable. "A man's reach should exceed his grasp"—yes, but not by too much. The piling up in the child of guilt and shame can create a burden that will last for life. The discrepancies between behavior and conscience or the existence of an immature conscience usually form a chronic source of hostility.

The difficulties of the toddler may be those of an experimenter. The selfishness of the young adolescent may be a stage of growth. The sex interest of the growing youth is not necessarily wickedness but preparation for establishing a mature sexual relationship and for parenthood. *A pura omnia pures*—to the pure all things are pure. The parent must try to see the adult growing in the child, and in so doing attempt to seek a balance in the ideals set before him. If training is forced upon the child too early, too harshly, or too constantly, his spirit can be crushed; if training comes too late, too leniently, or too little, the child may become impulse-ridden, lacking secure, automatic controls. Such an individual is a likely candidate for accepting immature, even criminal behavior. If training is too inflexible, it

may result in an adult so rigid that he will break down for lack
of adaptability; if it is inconsistent, it can produce constant vac-
illation and confusion. But if the ideals are those of emotional
maturity, then the conscience aids a balanced, harmonious development and good interpersonal relations—and life is, after
all, mostly human relations.

A fifth common source of hostility is displaced revenge for any
and all sorts of mistreatment, deliberate or unintentional, during childhood. Probably parental hostility to the child is the
greatest single source of the lifelong hatreds and readiness to
violence that we see so widely in adults. The dense fog of senti-
ment enshrouding parental love hides much of the stupidity, rejection, and abuse to which small children on all levels of society
are subjected.

Parents, unknowingly, frequently incite a child to anger and
aggressive behavior and then punish it for this reaction. Most
commonly this occurs because of failure to understand the
child's nature and development, by causing demands to be
made upon the child beyond its capacities. But a second important cause is the mishandling of the natural rivalries that exist
with parents and with brothers and sisters.

Guidance in cooperation is the answer to a fist fight between
two young brothers—not another verbal or physical battle between parent and the children involved. Some thought should
also be given to the parent's role in the fight—too often, all unwittingly, the parent's love is the object over which the children
are really battling. Children who are predominantly hostile are
sending up storm signals of the greatest importance; they must
be handled with increased understanding rather than force. For
the child he once was lives on in the adult, and so do the imagoes
of those who reared him.

To return to the basic question of what a mature parent-child
relationship should be, let us now consider some of its general
aspects. As we have already noted, the key to what is mature as
distinct from what is immature lies in the overall contrast between the parents' feelings and behavior toward the child and

the child's feelings and behavior toward the parents. The child receives, but the parents must give.

The child, at first, cooperates only to fill his needs. However, through accepting love and through identification with those who give him love, he learns to give it, to grow into his place in the family unit and to enjoy contributing there. All training should be designed to free the child's potentials for love, cooperation, and responsibility. For maturing is a process of growing from the passive, receptive, dependent attitudes and feelings of the child toward the parent into the responsible, productive, independent ones of the parent toward the child.

Parents often ask: "Is it all right to give the child a spanking if it is mild?" Such a question is probably beside the point. The essential is a good emotional relationship with the child and a good model of behavior for the child. It is possible for a parent to spank a child but to do it in such a way that the child feels justly treated. It is also possible for a parent never to spank a child, but by tone and manner to create such feelings of shame and guilt in the child that his opinion of himself is warped. This child may come to think of himself as a most inferior creature and this, as we have seen, is a prime source of fear and hostility. When parents react with vengefulness, it eventually destroys any possibility of a good relationship and will sow seeds in the child of lasting hate, with all its dire consequences for the child later in life and for the society. The child will tend much more to do what the parent does than what the parent says.

In this sense *what* is done is of much less importance than *how* it is done. The parent who is able to keep the child's love and friendship and to provide him with a good model for mature behavior has laid the foundation in that child for the capacity to love and be friendly throughout life. The parent who understands and trusts the course of development, who expects the good rather than the bad, will get it. And the question of spanking will not arise, for it misses the point.

So long as parents have genuine good feelings for their child and respect it as a person, there will be a responsive core of healthy good feelings in the child, which will provide it with the underlying capacity for good relationships with others. The child responds to love and confidence with love and confidence and, through identification, takes over these feelings and attitudes, modeling himself upon those who care for him. This is his great safeguard—and the parents'—against too extreme warpings of development and emotional disorders.

Love is the indispensable essence. Everyone needs love—enormously and desperately. We cannot go after it without realizing that if we are to get it others must give it. Love means an unselfish interest in the loved one for that one's own sake alone, for no ulterior motive. The reward to the parent comes not from exploiting the child in some way during childhood or later, nor from molding it to his or her own wishes. It comes only from the satisfaction of seeing the child develop and live out its life as a healthy and truly mature adult.

Chapter 14

FIGHTING THE DEVIL AND SEEKING THE GRAIL

Although hostility is a widespread and malignant disease which underlies many serious social and personal problems, there are powerful curative forces on the side of mankind in efforts to deal with this malady. The drives of the organism provide a biological basis for behavior that is constructive for the individual and the species. Ethics, good will, healthy family life —these are not artificial ideals foisted upon us by the necessities of civilization. On the contrary, they are expressions of our basic mature nature. They are the results of adult strength, even as hostility signifies frustration and weakness. Such constructive personal and social forces are strengthened by a tendency toward the evolution of higher forms. We know that phylogenetically there has been progress up the scale from peck orders to true leadership. Civilization itself and what we broadly call "mental development" or "culture" can be seen as part of

the evolutionary process, and this process is an aid to the sublimation and control, and, we hope, resolution of man's hostilities. Increasing clinical and experimental evidence that the
thrust toward maturity and cooperation can overcome the more
primitive fight-flight reflex bears this out. The problem thus appears to be one of education and social engineering—how to accomplish on a worldwide scale what is already being done by
proper therapeutic, psychodynamic treatment for individuals.

We have seen how faulty early conditioning produces lifelong
deformities of personality which, in turn, generate hostility. But
conditioning is something controllable. This has been proved
without question in experiments and field research with animals. On a human emotional level, reconditioning is seen daily
in psychoanalytic practice. A neurosis is essentially a persisting
pattern of a disturbed childhood emotional relationship to parents (and perhaps siblings). It is essentially a repetition and con-
tinuation of this relationship, more or less internalized as an in-
terrelationship between the superego and the rest of the personality, and more or less transferred to other persons. The patient
also "transfers" this relationship to his analyst, each session
providing the doctor with a sort of laboratory sample of the patient's relations to other persons, a sample of his key imagoes
and reaction patterns. The therapeutic task, then, is to correct
these imagoes and patterns and thus reopen emotional growth.

Progress toward cure is achieved by exposing the pattern of
infantile motivations to the patient's highest powers—to his ego
—his reason, reality sense, experience, judgment. In the process
the analyst comes to replace the authority of the parents. The
tendency of the person being analyzed to put himself in the position of a submissive, dependent child toward the analyst, as he
once was toward his parents, is unconscious and automatic. The
analyst cannot prevent it, but it is his responsibility to correct
and reduce it in favor of the patient's independence and maturity. As the analyst succeeds in altering these disordered childlike
feelings, the patient reduces the image of himself as an insecure,
guilty child in a world of controlling adults, ceases putting himself emotionally in such a position toward others, and comes to
see himself as he is through the eyes of the analyst, as a person

with mature powers for work and love and the capacity to enjoy them in a mature fashion.

Whatever the improper childhood conditioning, the analyst must make repeatedly clear to the patient the distinction between the patterns of reaction formed during early childhood and the present reality. He must constantly confront the patient with his tendency to react to the treatment situation, to others, and to himself in terms of this early conditioning and these imagoes. He must show that what was logical, appropriate behavior when the patient was a child and helpless may be unrealistic and unworkable in the present. Only in this way can the patient learn to see himself in his adult makeup, with his mature powers and the capacity for pleasure in exercising them. Only in this way can he learn to see others as they are in reality.

Analysis frees the ego from the tyranny of fixed, automatic, unconscious, infantile patterns. Understanding these patterns is the first step in this re-education, and continues as an essential. But insight alone is usually not sufficient. The central technique for correcting the personality fault is transference, that is, the repetition of childhood patterns to the analyst. The infantile is "analyzed out," so to speak, and the mature is freed so that emotional growth can take place through life experience.

The means of treatment followed by the analyst suggest the growth patterns to be adopted by the generally healthy in seeking emotional maturity and in the handling of their hostilities. More than a purely intellectual comprehension of the goals sought and the hazards to be overcome must be achieved by the individual, however, if growth is to occur, for some feeling-insight must accompany the mental processes if they are truly to be effective.

The question is whether it is possible for an individual to re-channel intellectually, for himself, by himself, unconscious impulses? It would seem that the answer is no—that what is unconscious in each individual cannot be raised to the conscious level solely by his own deliberate efforts. But before this is taken to mean that it is futile to think a man can attempt new growth alone, let us note that the intellect can probably aid this development. It is possible, therefore, that any man or woman seeking greater strength, higher goals, and a deeper capacity for mature love might find help in consistently educating himself toward these goals and in holding within himself at all times a vision of the ideal. Such a person may then be better prepared to benefit from insight, should it occur, for he will know what to look for in himself and be in a better position to learn from life, literature, and science and to develop his mature powers.

In what ways and to what extent different persons can help themselves has not yet been sufficiently explored scientifically. A severe warping of the personality will never, in all likelihood, be corrected by reading a book. Nevertheless we can realistically hope and expect that much will be gained as people come to recognize the roots of emotional disorders and hence of social disorders, as they come to appreciate what maturity consists of and how indispensable it is for satisfying living, and as they grasp and learn to apply the essential principles of child rearing. We can anticipate a happier world as this knowledge is clarified and disseminated and gradually finds a place in our ideology and in practical living.

One of the most important and pressing problems that each individual must face in his day-to-day experience is that of achieving a truly balanced way of life—that is, a life in which the give and the get, the progressive and the regressive, are in equilibrium. The meaning and implications of such a mode of life are so significant for enjoyment and for the reductions of hostility that they are worth looking at closely.

The logic of a balanced life derives from our knowledge, incomplete though it is at present, of the two opposing directions taken in everyone by his or her motivational forces. Biologically, the progressive forces impel the organism toward mature, productive, responsible, interdependent efforts, making a happy family and a happy society. But the forces grouped as regressive urge the organism to relinquish such productive, creative, working effort, and to return to the more passive, receptive, dependence of fetal life, infancy, and childhood.

Like chemical anabolism and catabolism, both tendencies are essential to life. Probably no animal organism has been found which can exist in maturity without some independent effort;

even forms so completely parasitic that they neither have nor need mouths to nourish themselves, nevertheless must expend some nonegocentric energy for reproduction to continue their species. In the higher forms the centrifugal output for the sake of mate, young, and social order is usually quite evident. But conversely, all energy output and no re-creation of energy is inconsistent with living. Rest, eating, sleeping, play, and the like are necessary self-indulgences and forms of normal essential regression seen throughout the animal kingdom.

For modern man, especially in times of economic difficulty, life has become largely the art of getting these two opposing forces into balance. This balance involves not only going through the motions of adequate amounts of work and play, but also genuine, deep enjoyment of both these progressive and regressive activities. While, socially speaking, we instinctively distrust either extreme—the playboy or the loafer at one end, and the harried, compulsive slave-driver at the other—there are many reasons why modern man finds the balanced life difficult to achieve. Even what should be sport or play often becomes respected only as work and people must frequently apologize for balancing duty with adequate recreation.

Of course much of the reason why individuals get trapped in this sort of an attitude stems from inner conflicts. But too many people who are neither neurotic nor conditioned to such patterns also fail to adopt the balanced life simply because they do not recognize its value in mature development and healthy living. We have all known people who when they worked longed for relaxation—and when they relaxed, felt they should be working. These people seem to have to force themselves to work and force themselves to play. Each tendency, the progressive and the regressive, drives head-on against the other; the two are never separated so that they can establish a balance and rhythm. Such people can enjoy neither work nor play; they should enjoy both.

Sometimes a partly healthy reaction of shame and self-defense against an overindulgent childhood drives a man or woman into compulsive working. Frequently guilt and the need for self-punishment may be the unconscious motivation for too much or too little work. But very common causes are simply our present emphasis on the prestige that goes hand in hand with getting—especially the getting of money. The virtues of healthy ambition are often lost in the excesses. How frequently is the sleepless struggle for "happiness" mistranslated into dollar terms, only to bring suffering, breakdown, a broken home, ulcers, coronary thrombosis, and high blood pressure.

For nature will not be outsmarted. We are born to a certain mold and our development follows nature's pattern; we age, mature, and decline according to her laws. The only happiness and power lie in understanding and going along with the forces that shape and control us and in whose inexorable grip we are. Vanity and pride are ludicrous in the face of the overwhelmingly powerful realities of biology and of the universe, the underlying forces of which made us and use us for their expression. To obstruct their ability to help us make use of our mature powers to love sexually and socially and to make a harmonious society, is inevitably to pay the price in emotional disorders and their consequences.

Thus knowledge has accumulated of the proper course of human development, of what constitutes maturity and of the inevitable problems which, with guidance, the child must solve if he is to grow up adequately and to enjoy living out his life in the full expression of his mature, constructive powers, with all that this means to himself, his family, his nation, his species.

To this basic knowledge, all the physiological, biological, and social sciences can contribute. Because of the overlapping of the various fields, interdisciplinary teams should be especially effective. Much more work should be done in this area within the scientific community than is going on at present. Existing scientific societies could well serve this goal by establishing special sections for the investigation of how to grow better human beings. At present more is done to study and achieve the growth of hogs and cattle than of men. Efforts should be made to bring together all scientists who share this interest, as the national societies for cancer and heart disease have done. Individuals might be recruited from our educational system as well as the various related sciences to serve as researchers in this field. Ideally, a "Manhattan District Project" should be organized for the study of human development and for combating its chief obstruction, man's hostility to man. The growing body of knowledge could then be made constructively effective through school, church, and state. If a tiny fraction of what is spent on armaments were spent on studying human destructiveness and human constructiveness, then just as science has reduced for us the terrors of inanimate nature and even of disease, it might show us how to reduce the terrors of that threatening disease of hostility within man himself.

Through advances in the physical sciences we are developing an amazing technology of production, distribution, communication, and transportation. We can expect that in time social scientists—the economists, political scientists, sociologists, and others—will help us to improve social organization. The power of circumstance is obvious. The stresses, insecurities, anxieties, complexities with which adults struggle to maintain themselves and their families and establish a place in society influence everyone. Full solution cannot come from increasing improvements in social organization alone, for at the bottom, the most perfect organization consists of people and will not operate maturely unless the individual men and women who constitute it are sufficiently mature. Organization, in fact, should be directed toward achieving the proper development of children and the proper conditions of life for mature adults. The epiorganism always reflects the characteristics of the unit organisms that compose it; our bodies have the earmarks of our cells; our society bears witness to the individuals within it.

Our times are marked by a great paradox: man tends to use his enormously increased power over nature much less for his good than for his destruction. Thus, for example, the dream that science might tap the power of the atom has brought us, not rejoicing over new wealth and new security, but fear of total destruction. This paradox springs from the fact that each individual in our society is activated by strong asocial or antisocial motivations as well as by social ones. Survival has become a matter of understanding these two sets of impulses in order to aid the constructive and prohuman, and to reduce the destructive, and antihuman motivations. To seek emotional security and thereby

secure what is prohuman, is to seek the grail; the devil is the in-
carnation of evil, and evil is disordered infantile impulses, chief
of all man's hostility to man.

Hostility can be attacked at its roots: in the rearing of the
child and in the re-education of the adult. It can be banished as
smallpox and typhoid have been banished in this country. Then
we shall realize the dream of producing mature, constructive
men and women so that there may be many of them among us.
The ancient war of good against evil, of love against hate, of God
against Devil, of democracy against tyranny, is also the war of
the mature and loving people against the infantile and hostile
people. In this struggle lies humanity's most thrilling challenge;
in the outcome lies the hope of a desperate world.

Man's inhumanity to man springs almost entirely from irrational sources. Today the individual cannot meet his difficulties
by physical attack and neither can nations. War is basically and
ultimately irrational. Our survival on this planet is possible only
through cooperation, responsibility, productivity, and interdependence. The fight-flight reaction as a method for solving the
complex problems of modern social adjustment among individuals or nations is like trying to repair a fine watch with a hammer.

Hostility should be made universally known for what it is: a
neurotic symptom, a symptom of weakness and frustration, a
primitive method of defense, which has become mankind's
principal enemy and threatens to destroy him. We should know
that a Nero and a Hitler and other such monsters are made, not
born, that evil and violence have their genesis in the mishandling of the emotions, that they are preventable perversions.

The problem should be tackled by all the related sciences. It
should be pursued at least as widely and energetically as the
physiological diseases, such as cancer and heart disease. Our
best brains should be mobilized and given adequate funds to attack this problem on a national scale. What is already known
should be disseminated systematically and as widely as possible
to improve the upbringing of our children and thereby the lives
of our adults. In the long run our security will not rest with a sophisticated and computer-controlled weaponry but with a

population that is strong, realistic, and resourceful, through its achievement of emotional maturity. The best available information should be made readily accessible through libraries, mass media, schools, churches, and all those who deal with people and particularly with children.

And what if, in considering national and international policies, the central issue were always kept in mind of how this would affect the children of the world during their most crucial formative years from conception to age six? The greatest single effort of the nation and of the world should be devoted to seeing that its children mature emotionally from the moment of conception. This is the basic answer to man's tendency to torture and destroy himself. The practical difficulties *can* be overcome. When they are, peace and brotherhood will be, not sentimental dreams, but practical reality, and man will have saved himself from being a far more spectacular biological failure than the dinosaur.

SELECTED BIBIOGRAPHY

Abrahamsen, D. *The Murdering Mind*. New York: Harper & Row, 1973.

_____. *Our Violent Society*. New York: Funk & Wagnalls, 1970.

_____. *The Psychology of Crime*. New York: Columbia Univ. Press, 1960.

Ackerman, N. W. Disturbances of mothering and criteria for treatment. *Amer. J. Orthopsychiat.* 26 (1956): 252-263.

_____ *The Psychodynamics of Family Life*. New York: Basic Books, 1958.

Adler, A. *The Practice and Theory of Individual Psychology*. New York: Harcourt, Brace and Jovanovich, 1924.

Adler, G. Prison treatment: past, present and future. *Psychiatric Opinion* 9 (1972): 6-10.

Adorno, T. W., Frenkel-Brunswick, W., et al. *The Authoritarian Personality*. New York: Harper & Row, 1950.

Aichhorn, A. *Delinquency and Child Guidance: Selected Papers*. Edited by O. Fleishman, P. Kramer, and H. Ross. New York: Internat. Univ. Press, 1964.

_____. *Wayward Youth*. New York: Viking, 1935.

Alexander, F. *Fundamentals of Psychoanalysis*. New York: W. W. Norton, 1948.

_____. The neurotic character. *Internat. J. Psychoanal.* 2 (1930): 293.

_____. *Our Age of Unreason.* Philadelphia: Lippincott, 1942.

_____. *Psychosomatic Medicine.* New York: W. W. Norton, 1950.

_____. *The Scope of Psychoanalysis.* New York: Basic Books, 1961.

_____. *The Western Mind in Transition.* New York: Random House, 1960.

Alexander, F., and French, T. *Psychoanalytic Therapy.* New York: Ronald Press, 1942.

Alexander, F. and Healy, W. *Roots of Crime: Psychoanalytic Studies.* New York: Alfred A. Knopf, 1935.

Alexander, F. and Ross, H. *Dynamic Psychiatry.* Chicago: Univ. of Chicago Press, 1952.

Allee, W. C. *Co-operation Among Animals.* New York: Schuman, 1951.

Allen, M. A cross-cultural study of aggression and crime. *J. of Cross-Cult. Psych.* 3 (1972): 259-271.

Alpert, A. Reversibility of pathological fixations associated with maternal deprivation in infancy. In *The Psychoanalytic Study of the Child*, 14: 169-185. New York: Internat. Univ. Press, 1959.

Altman, C. H. Relation between maternal attitudes and child's personality structure. *Amer. J. Orthopsychiat.* 28 (1958): 160-169.

Alvarez, A. *The Savage God, A Study of Suicide.* New York: Random House, 1970.

Amanat, E., and Eble, S. Marriage role conflicts and child psychopathology. *Adolescence* 8 (1973): 575-588.

Anderson, J. E. *Experience and Behavior in Early Childhood and the Adjustment of the Same Persons as Adults.* Minneapolis: Univ. of Minnesota, Instit. of Child Development, 1963.

Anderson, R. E. Where's Dad? Paternal deprivation and delinquency. *Arch. Gen. Psychiat.* 18 (1968): 641-649.

Andrey, R. G. *Delinquency and Parental Pathology.* London: Metheun, 1960.

Anthony E. J., and Benedek, T., eds. *Parenthood: Its Psychology and Psychopathology.* Boston: Little, Brown, 1970.

Arenendt, H. *On Violence.* New York: Harcourt, Brace and Jovanovich, 1970.

Ausubel, D. P. *Theory and Problems of Child Development.* New York: Grune & Stratton, 1958.

Bach-y-Rita, G., Lion, J. R., Climent, C. E., and Ervin, F. R. Episodic dyscontrol: A study of 130 violent patients. *Amer. J. Psychiat.* 127 (1971): 1473-1478.

Bach-y-Rita, G., and Veno, A. Habitual violence: A profile of 62 men. *Amer. J. Psychiat.* 131 (1974): 1015-1017.

Bacon, M. K., Barry, H., and Child, I. L. A cross-cultural study of correlates of crime. *J. Abnorm. and Soc. Psychol.* 66 (1963): 291-300.

Bandura, A., and Walters, R. H. *Adolescent Aggression*. New York: Ronald Press, 1959.

_____. Dependency conflicts in aggressive delinquents. *J. Social Issues* 14 (1958): 52-65.

_____. *Social Learning and Personality Development*. New York: Holt, Rinehart and Winston, 1963.

Bastiaans, J. General comments on the role of aggression in human psychopathology. *Psychother. and Psychosom*. 20 (1972): 300-311.

Bayley, N., and Schafer, E. S. Maternal behavior and personality development data from the Berkeley Growth Study. *Psychiat. Research Rep*. 13 (1960): 155-175.

Beck, M. W. Abortion: The mental health consequences of unwantedness. In *Abortion, Changing Views and Practice*, edited by R. B. Sloane. New York: Grune & Stratton, 1971.

Becker, W. C., Peterson, D. R., Hellmer, L. A., Shoemaker, D. J., and Quay, H. C. Factors in parental behavior and personality as related to problem behavior in children. *J. Consult. Psychol*. 23 (1959): 107-118.

Bender, L. *Aggression, Hostility and Anxiety*. Philadelphia: Saunders, 1953.

_____. *A Dynamic Psychopathology of Childhood*. Springfield, Ill.: Charles C. Thomas, 1956.

_____. Genesis of hostility in children. *Amer. J. Psychiat*. 105 (1948): 241-245.

_____. Genesis of hostility in children. *Psychoanal. Rev*. 50 (1963): 95-102.

_____. Psychopathic behavior disorders in children. In *Handbook of Correctional Psychology*, edited by R. M. Lindner and R. V. Seliger. New York: Philosophical Library, 1947.

Benedict, R. *Patterns of Culture*. Boston: Houghton Mifflin, 1934.

Beris, D. Vicissitudes of superego functions and superego precursors in childhood. In *The Psychoanalytic Study of the Child*, vol. 13. New York: Internat. Univ. Press, 1958.

Berkowitz, L. *Aggression: A Social Psychological Analysis*. New York: McGraw-Hill, 1962.

_____, ed. *Roots of Aggression: A Re-examination of the Frustration-Aggression Hypothesis*. New York: Atherton Press, 1969.

_____. Some factors affecting the reduction of overt hostility. *J. Abnorm. and Soc. Psychol*. 60 (1960): 14-21.

Bird, B. A consideration of the etiology of prejudice. *J. Amer. Psychoanal. Assn*. 5 (1957): 490-513.

Boisvert, M. J. The battered-child syndrome. *Social Casework* 53 (1972): 475-480.

Bowlby, J. A. Ethology and the development of object relations. *Internat. J. Psycho-Anal*. 41 (1960): 313-317.

_____. The nature of the child's tie to his mother. *Internat. J. Psycho-Anal.* 39 (1958): 350-373.

_____. Separation anxiety. *Internat. J. Psycho-Anal.* 41 (1960): 89-113.

Bowlby, J. A., Ainsworth, M., Boston, M., and Rosenbluth, D. The effects of mother-child separation. *Brit. J. Med. Psychol.* 29 (1956): 211-247.

Bramson, L., and Goethals, G. W., eds. *War: Studies from Psychology, Sociology and Anthropology.* New York: Basic Books, 1964.

Bromberg, W. Dynamic aspects of psychopathic personality. *Psychoanal. Quart.* 17 (1948): 48-70.

Bronson, W. C. Central orientations: a study of behavior organization from childhood to adolescence. *Child Dev.* 37 (1966): 125-155.

_____. Stable patterns of behavior: The significance of enduring orientations for personality development. In *Minnesota Symposia on Child Psychology*, vol. 2. Minneapolis: Univ. of Minnesota Press, 1969.

Brosin, H. W. Evolution and understanding diseases of the mind. In *Evolution after Darwin*, vol. 2, edited by S. Tax. Chicago: Univ. of Chicago Press, 1960.

_____. Human aggression in psychiatric perspective. In *Aggression and Defense—Neural Mechanisms and Social Patterns (Brain Function)*, vol. 5, edited by C. D. Clemente and D. B. Lindsley. Berkeley and Los Angeles: Univ. of Calif. Press, 1967.

Brown, D. *Bury My Heart at Wounded Knee.* New York: Holt, Rinehart & Winston, 1970.

Buss, A. H. *Psychology of Aggression.* New York: Wiley, 1961.

Button, A. Some antecedents of felonious and delinquent behavior, *J. of Clin. Child Psychol.* 2 (1973): 35-37.

Bychowski, G. *Evil in Man: The Anatomy of Hate and Violence.* New York: Grune & Stratton, 1968.

_____. Patterns of anger. In *The Psychoanalytic Study of the Child*, 21: 172-192. New York: Internat. Univ. Press, 1966.

_____. Psychopathology of aggression and violence. *Bull. N.Y. Acad. Med.* 43 (1967): 300-309.

_____. Struggle against the introjects. *Internat. J. Psychoanal.* 39 (1958): 182.

Bylinsky, G. Violence. *Fortune* (Jan. 1973): 135-146.

Cannon, W. B. *Bodily Changes in Fear, Hunger, Pain, and Rage.* New York: Appleton, 1929.

Carrighar, S. *Wild Heritage.* Boston: Houghton Mifflin, 1965.

Carthy, J. D., and Ebling, F. J., eds. *The Natural History of Aggression.* New York: Academic Press, 1964.

Clark, L. D. A comparative view of aggressive behavior. *Amer. J. Psychiat.* 119 (1962): 336-341.

Cline, V. B., and Wangrow, A. S. Female criminals: Their personal, familial, and social backgrounds: The relation of these to the diagnosis of sociopathy and hysteria. *Arch. Gen. Psychiat.* 23 (1970): 554-558.

Cohen, F. S. The relationship between delusional thinking and hostility—A case study. *Psychiat. Quart.* 30 (1956): 115.

Cohen, F. J., ed. *Youth and Crime.* New York: Internat. Univ. Press, 1957.

Comfort, A. *Authority and Delinquency in the Modern State.* London: Routledge & Kegan Paul, 1950.

Corning, P. A., and Corning, C. H. Toward a general theory of violent aggression. *Social Science Infor.* 11 (1972): 7-35.

Craft, M. *Ten Studies into Psychopathic Personalities.* Bristol, England: Wright, 1965.

Daniels, D. N., and Gilula, M. F. Violence and the struggle for existence. In *Violence and the Struggle for Existence*, edited by D. N. Daniels, M. F. Gilula, and F. M. Ochberg. Boston: Little, Brown, 1970.

Daniels, D. N., Gilula, M. F., and Ochberg, F. M., eds. *Violence and the Struggle for Existence.* Boston: Little, Brown, 1970.

Daniels, G. E. Approaches to a biological basis of human behavior. *Diseases of the Nerv. Sys.* 32 (1971): 227-239.

_____. Comprehensive medicine. In *Changing Concepts of Psychoanalytic Medicine*, edited by S. Rado and G. E. Daniels. New York: Grune & Stratton, 1956.

Darwin, C. R. *The Expression of Emotions in Man and Animals.* Chicago: Univ. of Chicago Press, 1965.

De Hartog, J. *The Peaceable Kingdom.* New York: Atheneum, 1971.

DeJong, H. H. *Experimental Catatonia.* Baltimore: Williams & Wilkins, 1945.

De Rosis, H. A. Violence: where does it begin? *Family Coordinator* 20 (1971): 355-362.

Di Tullio, B. The causes of criminality. *Monographs of the Criminal Law Education and Research Center* 3 (1969): 53-70.

_____. Criminogenesis. *Monographs of the Criminal Law Education and Research Center* 3 (1969): 119-146.

_____. The relationship between mental illness and criminal behavior. *Monographs of the Criminal Law, Education and Research Center* 3 (1969): 37-52.

Dollard, J., et al. *Frustration and Aggression.* New Haven: Yale Univ. Press, 1939.

Donnelly, J. Aspects of the psychodynamics of the psychopath. *Amer. J. Psychiat.* 120 (1964): 1149-1153.

Du Bos, R. *Man Adapting.* New Haven: Yale Univ. Press, 1965.

_____ *Man, Medicine and Environment.* New York: Praeger, 1968.

_____. *So Human an Animal.* New York: Scribner's, 1968.

Duncan, G. M., Frazier, S. H., Litin, E. M., Johnson, A. M., and Barron, A. Etiological factors in first-degree murder. *J.A.M.A.* 168 (1958): 1755-1758.

Eibl-Eibesfeldt, I. *Love and Hate: The Natural History of Behavior Patterns,* translated by G. Strachan. New York: Holt, Rinehart & Winston, 1972.

Eisner, V. *The Delinquency Label: The epidemiology of Juvenile Delinquency.* New York: Random House, 1969.

Eissler, K. R., ed. *Searchlights on Delinquency.* New York: Internat. Univ. Press, 1949.

English, O. S., and Pearson, G. H. J. *Emotional Problems of Living.* New York: Norton, 1955.

Erikson, E. H. *Childhood and Society,* 2nd ed. New York: Norton, 1969.

_____. *Identity and the Life Cycle.* New York: Internat. Univ. Press, 1959.

_____. Psychoanalysis and ongoing history: Problems of identity, hatred and violence. *Amer. J. Psychiat.* 122 (1965): 241-250.

Fawcett, J., ed. *Dynamics of Violence.* Chicago: A.M.A., 1971.

Feldhusen, J. F., Thurston, J. R., and Benning, J. J. Studying aggressive children through responses to frustrating situations. *Child Study J.* 2 (1971): 1-17.

Fenby, T. P. The work of the National Society for the Prevention of Cruelty to Children (N.S.P.C.C.). *Internat. J. of Offender Therapy and Comparative Criminology* 16 (1972): 201-205.

Ferenczi, S. *Stages in the Development of the Sense of Reality in Sex or Psychoanalysis.* New York: Basic Books, 1950.

Feshbach, N. D. The effects of violence in childhood. *J. of Clin. Child Psychol.* 2 (1973): 28-31.

Feshbach, S. Dynamics and morality of violence and aggression: Some psychological considerations. *Amer. Psychol.* 26 (1971): 281-292.

Fine, R. The stress of peace. In *The Emotional Stress of War, Violence, and Peace,* edited by R. S. Parker. Pittsburgh: Stanwix House, 1972.

Fisher, R. D., ed. *International Conflict and Behavioral Science.* New York: Basic Books, 1964.

Fleming, P., and Ricks, D. F. Emotions of children before schizophrenia and before character disorder. In *Life History Research in Psychopathology,* vol. 1., edited by M. Roff and D. F. Ricks. Minneapolis: Univ. of Minnesota Press, 1970.

Forer, L. G. The rights of children. *Young Children* 27 (1972): 332-339.

Freeman, D. Human aggression in anthropological perspective. In *The Natural History of Aggression,* edited by J. D. Carthy and F. J. Ebling. New York: Academic Press, 1964.

French, T. M. *Psychoanalytic Interpretations.* Chicago: Quadrangle Books, 1970.

_____. *Selected Papers.* Chicago: Quadrangle Books, 1970.

_____. Social conflict and psychic conflict. *Amer. J. Soc.* 44 (1939): 922.

Freud, A. Aggression in relation to emotional development: Normal and pathological. In *The Psychoanalytic Study of the Child,* vols. 3 and 4. New York: Internat. Univ. Press, 1949.

Freud, A., and Burlingham, D. *War and Children*. New York: Internat. Univ. Press, 1943.

Freud, S. Certain neurotic mechanisms in jealousy, paranoia, and homosexuality. *Collected Papers*, vol. 2. London: Hogarth Press, 1924.

_____. *Civilization and Its Discontents*. London: Hogarth Press, 1930.

_____. *A General Introduction to Psychoanalysis*. Garden City, N.Y.: Garden City Publ. Co., 1943.

_____. *Group Psychology and Analysis of the Ego*. New York: Liveright, 1949.

_____. *An Outline of Psychoanalysis*. New York: Norton, 1949.

_____. *Totem and Taboo*. New York: Moffat, 1918.

Fried, E. Ego strengthening aspects of hostility. *Amer. J. Orthopsychiat.* 26 (1956): 179-187.

Fries, M. E. Problems of early development. In *The Psychoanalytic Study of the Child*, vol. 8. New York: Internat. Univ. Press, 1953.
lationships. *J. Amer. Psychoanal. Assn.* 9 (1961): 669-683.

Fromm, E. Man would as soon flee as fight. *Psychology Today* 7 (1973): 35-39, 41-45.

Galvin, J. Some dynamics of delinquent girls. *J. Nerv. and Ment. Dis.* 123 (1956): 292-295.

Ganth, W. H., ed. *Physiological Basis of Psychiatry*. Springfield, Ill.: Charles C. Thomas, 1958.

Gillespie, W. H. Aggression and instinct theory. *Internat. J. Psychoanal.* 52 (1971): 155-160.

Gilula, M. F., and Daniels, D. N. Violence and man's struggle to adapt. *Science* 164 (1969): 396-405.

Glover, E. Psychoanalysis and criminology. *Internat. J. Psychoanal.* 37 (1956): 311-317.

_____. *Roots of Crime*. New York: Internat. Univ. Press, 1960.

Glueck, B. C., Jr. Psychodynamic patterns in the sexual offender: mechanisms of conscience formation. In *Changing Concepts of Psychoanalytic Medicine*, edited by S. Rado and G. E. Daniels. New York: Grune & Stratton, 1956.

Glueck, S., and Glueck, E. *Unravelling Juvenile Delinquency*. Cambridge, Mass.: Harvard Univ. Press, 1950.

Goldston, I. Psychiatry for the millions. In *Techniques of Therapy*, edited by J. Masserman. New York: Grune & Stratton, 1971.

Goodall, J. *In the shadow of Man*. Boston: Houghton Mifflin, 1971.

Gray, P. H. Theory and evidence of imprinting in human infants. *J. Psychol.* 48 (1958): 155-156.

Greenacre, P. *Emotional Growth*, 2 vols. New York: *Internat. Univ. Press*, 1971.

_____. Considerations regarding the parent-infant relationship. *Internat. J. Psychoanal.* 41 (1960): 571-584.

Greenberg, H. R., and Blank, R. H. Murder and self-destruction by a twelve-year-old boy. *Adolescence* 5 (1970): 391-396.

Greenberg, N. H. Studies of psychosomatic differentation during infancy. A longitudinal anterospective approach for the study of development during infancy. *Arch. Gen. Psychiat.* 7 (1962): 389-406.

Grier, W., and Cobbs, P. *Black Rage.* New York: Basic Books, 1968.

Grinker, R. R. What is the cause of violence? In *Dynamics of Violence,* edited by J. Fawcett. Chicago: A.M.A., 1971.

Guntrip, H. *Personality Structure and Human Interaction.* New York: Internat. Univ. Press, 1961.

_____. *Psychoanalytic Theory, Therapy, and the Self.* New York: Basic Books, 1971.

Halleck, S. L. *Psychiatry and the Dilemmas of Crime: A Study of Causes, Punishment and Treatment.* New York: Hoeber Med. Div., Harper & Row, 1967.

Hallowell, A. I. Self, society and culture in phylogenetic perspective. In *Evolution after Darwin,* vol. 2, edited by S. Tax. Chicago; univ. of Chicago Press, 1960.

Hamburg., D. A. Emotions in the perspective of human evolution. In *Expression of the Emotions in Man,* edited by P. D. Knapp. New York: Internat. Univ. Press, 1963.

_____. Ethological perspectives on human aggressive behavior. In *Ethology and Psychiatry,* edited by N. F. White. Toronto: Univ. of Toronto Press, 1974.

Harlow, H. F. Learning to love. *Amer. Scientist* 54 (1966): 244-272.

_____. Primary affectional patterns in primates. *Amer. J. Orthopsychiat.* 30 (1960): 676-684.

Hartmann, H. *Ego Psychology and the Problem of Adaptation.* New York: Internat. Univ. Press, 1958.

Hartmann, H., Kris, E., and Lowenstein, R. M. Notes on the theory of aggression. In *The Psychoanalytic Study of the Child.* 3: 9-36. New York: Internat. Univ. Press, 1949.

Haskins, C. *Of Societies and Men.* New York: Norton, 1953.

Havens, L. L. Youth, violence, and the nature of family life. *Psychiatric Annals* 2 (1972): 18-29.

Heimann, P., and Valenstein, A. F. The psychoanalytical concept of aggression: An integrated summary. *Internat. J. Psychoanal.* 53 (1972): 31-35.

Helfer, R. E., and Kempe, C. H. *The Battered Child.* Chicago: Univ. of Chicago Press, 1968.

Henry, J. *Pathways to Madness.* New York: Random House, 1971.

Herrick, C. J. *The Evolution of Human Nature.* Austin, Texas: Univ. of Texas Press, 1956.

Hess, E. H. Imprinting: Effects of early experience, imprinting determines later social behavior in animals. *Science* 130 (1959): 133-141.

Hinkle, L. E., Christenson, W. N., Kane, F. D., Osteld, A., Thetford, W. N., and Wolff, H. G. An investigation of the relation between life experience, personality characteristics, and general susceptibility to illness. *Psychosom. Med.* 20 (1958): 278-295.

Hokanson, J. E. The effects of guilt arousal and severity of discipline on adult aggressive behavior. *J. Clin. Psychol.* 17 (1961): 29-32.

Hough, R. *Captain Bligh and Mr. Christian.* New York: E. P. Dutton, 1970.

Ikemi, Y. A psychosomatic approach to aggressive patients. *Psychosomatics* 13 (1972): 155-157.

Ilfeld, F. W. Overview of the causes and prevention of violence. *Arch. Gen. Psychiat.* 20 (1969): 675-689.

Jenkins, R. M. The psychopathic or antisocial personality. *J. Nerv. and Ment. Dis.* 131 (1960): 318-334.

Jennings, H. S. The beginnings of social behavior in unicellular organisms. *Science* 92 (1940): 539.

Johnson, A. M. *Experience, Affect, and Behavior: Psychoanalytic Explorations of Doctor Adelaide McFayden Johnson*, edited by D. B. Robinson. Chicago: Univ. of Chicago Press, 1969.

_____ and Szurek, S. A. Etiology of antisocial behavior in delinquents and psychopaths. *J.A.M.A.* 154 (1954): 184-187.

_____. The genesis of antisocial acting out in children and adults. *Psychoanal. Quart.* 21 (1952): 323-343.

Jones, E. *The Life and Work of Sigmund Freud*, vol. 1. New York: Basic Books, 1952.

Kagan, J. Motives and development. *J. of Personality and Soc. Psychol.* 22 (1972): 51-66.

_____ and Moss, H. A. *Birth to Maturity: A Study in Psychological Development.* New York: John Wiley, 1962.

Kahn, E. Fear, hostility, reality. *Amer. J. Psychiat.* 115 (1959): 1002-1005.

Kalogerakis, M. G. Homicide in adolescents: Fantasy and deed. In *Dynamics of Violence*, edited by J. Fawcett. Chicago: A.M.A., 1971.

Kempe, C. H., and Helfer, R. E., eds. *Helping the Battered Child and His Family.* Philadelphia: Lippincott, 1972.

Kempe, C. H., Silverman, F. N., Steele, B. F., Droegemuller, W., and Silver, H. K. The battered-child syndrome. *J.A.M.A.* 181 (1962): 17-24.

Keniston, K. Violence: Sadism and cataclysm. In *Violence in America*, edited by T. Rose. New York: Random House, 1970.

Kestemberg, E., rptr. Panel: The role of aggression in child analysis. *Internat. J. Psychoanal.* 53 (1972): 321-323.

Kogan, K. L., and Wimberger, H. C. Behavior transactions between disturbed children and their mothers. *Psychol. Rpts.* 28 (1971): 395-404.

Kolb, L. C. Violence and aggression—an overview. In *Dynamics of Violence*, edited by J. Fawcett. Chicago: A.M.A., 1971.

Kurth, G. M. Hitler's two Germanies; a sidelight on nationalism. In *Psychoanalysis and the Social Sciences*, edited by G. Roheim. New York: Internat. Univ. Press, 1947.

_____. The Jew and Adolph Hitler. *Psychoanal. Quart.* 16 (1947): 11-32.

Lampl-DeGroot, J. Neurotics, delinquents and ideal formation. In *Searchlights on Delinquency*, edited by K. Eissler. New York: Internat. Univ. Press, 1949.

_____. Psychoanalysis and its relation to certain other fields of natural science. *Internat. J. Psycho-Anal.* 40 (1958): 169-179.

Langer, W. C. *The Mind of Adolph Hitler—The Secret Wartime Report.* New York: Basic Books, 1972.

Langner, H. The making of a murderer. *Amer. J. Psychiat.* 127 (1971): 950-953.

Laury, G. V., and Meerloo, J. A. Mental cruelty and child abuse. *Psychiat. Quart. Suppl.* 41 (1967): 203-254.

Lesse, S. Psychodynamic relationships between degree of anxiety and other clinical symptoms. *J. Nerv. and Ment. Dis.* 127 (1958): 124-130.

Lester, D. Suicide: aggression or hostility? *Crisis Intervention* 3 (1971): 10-14.

Levine, S. The effects of experience on adult behavior. In *Experimental Foundations of Clinical Psychology*, edited by A. J. Bachrach. New York: Basic Books, 1962.

_____. Infantile experiences and resistance to physiological stress. *Science* 126 (1957): 405.

Liddell, H. S. A biological basis for psychopathology. In *Problems of Addiction and Habituation*, edited by P. H. Hoch and J. Zubin. New York: Grune & Stratton, 1958.

_____. *Emotional Hazards in Animals and Man.* Springfield, Ill.: Charles C. Thomas, 1956.

Livson, N., and Peskin, H. Prediction of adult psychological health in a longitudinal study. *J. Abnorm. Psychol.* 72 (1967): 509-518.

Loewenstein, R. M., ed. *Drives, Affects, Behavior.* New York: Internat. Univ. Press, 1953.

Lorenz, K. *On Aggression.* New York: Harcourt, Brace and Jovanovich, 1966.

Lukas, J. A. *Don't Shoot: We Are Your Children.* New York: Dell, 1967.

Lukianowicz, N. Infanticide. *Psychiatria Clinica* 4 (1971): 145-158.

Lussier, A., rptr. Panel: Aggression. *Internat. J. Psycho-Anal.* 53 (1972): 13-19.

Macfarlane, J. W. From infancy to adulthood. *Childhood Educ.* 39 (1963): 336-342.

_____. Perspectives on personality consistency and change from the Guidance Study. *Vita Humana* 7 (1964): 115-126.

Madison, P. *Freud's Concept of Repression and Defense, Its Theoretical and Observational Language*. Minneapolis: Univ. of Minnesota Press, 1961.

Madoff, J. M. The attitudes of mothers of juvenile delinquents toward child rearing. *J. Consult. Psychol.* 23 (1959): 518-520.

Madow, L. *Anger*. New York: Scribner's, 1972.

Mahler, M. S. On the significance of the normal separation-individuation phase. In *Drives, Affects, Behavior*, edited by M. Schur. New York: Internat. Univ. Press, 1965.

―――. On human symbiosis and the vicissitudes of individuation. *J. Amer. Psychoanal. Assn.* 15 (1967): 740-763.

―――. *On Human Symbiosis and the Vicissitudes of Individuation*, vol. 1. New York: Internat. Univ. Press, 1968.

―――. Thoughts about development and individuation. In *The Psychoanalytic Study of the Child*, 18: 307-324. New York: Internat. Univ. Press, 1963.

Mahler, M. S., and Furer, M. Certain aspects of the separation-individuation phase. *Psychoanal. Quart.* 32 (1962): 1-14.

Mahler, M. S., and La Perriere, K. Mother-child interaction during separation-individual. *Psychoanal. Quart.* 34 (1965): 483-498.

Mandelbaum, G., and Mandelbaum, A. *Philosophic Problems*. New York: Macmillan, 1957.

Mark, V. J., and Ervin, F. *Violence and the Brain*. New York: Harper & Row, 1970.

Masserman, J. *Principles of Dynamic Psychiatry*. Philadelphia: Saunders, 1961.

―――. and Schwab, J., eds. *Man for Humanity, On Concordance vs. Discord in Human Behavior*. Springfield, Ill.: Charles C. Thomas, 1972.

May, R. *Power and Innocence: A Search for the Sources of Violence*. New York: Norton, 1972.

McCord, W., McCord, J., and Howard, A. Familial correlates of aggression in non-delinquent children. *J. of Abnorm. and Soc. Psychol.* 62 (1961): 79-93.

McCord, W., McCord, J., and Zola, I. K. *Origins of Crime*. New York: Columbia Univ. Press, 1959.

McCranie, E. J. Depression, anxiety and hostility. *Psychiat. Quart.* 45 (1971): 117-133.

McDevitt, J., and Settlage, C., eds. *Separation-Individuation*. New York: Internat. Univ. Press, 1971.

McNeil, E. B. Psychology and aggression. *J. Conflict Resolution* 3 (1959): 195-203.

Mead, M. Changing patterns of parent-child culture. *Internat J. Psycho-Anal.* 38 (1957): 369-378.

―――. *Continuities in Cultural Evolution*. New Haven: Yale Univ. Press, 1964.

_____. *Male and Female*. New York: William Morrow, 1949.

_____. *Sex and Temperament in Three Primitive Societies*. New York: William Morrow, 1935.

Mednick, S. A., and Schulsinger, F. Factors related to breakdown in children at high risk for schizophrenia. In *Life History Research in Psychopathology*, vol. 1, edited by M. Roff and D. F. Ricks. Minneapolis: Univ. of Minnesota Press, 1970.

Megargee, E. I., Hokanson, J. E., eds. *The Dynamics of Aggression: Individual, Group, and International Analyses*. New York: Harper & Row, 1970.

Menninger, R. W., and Modlin, H. C. Individual violence: prevention in the violence-threatening patient. In *Dynamics of Violence*, edited by J. Fawcett. Chicago: A.M.A., 1971.

Milgram, S. *Obedience to Authority: An experimental View*. New York: Harper & Row, 1973.

Moltz, H. Imprinting: empirical basis and theoretical significance. *Psychol. Bull.* 57 (1960): 291-314.

Morris, H. H., Jr., et al. Aggressive behavior disorders of children: a followup study. *Amer. J. Psychiat.* 112 (1956): 991-997.

Morrison, J. R., and Stewart, M. A. A family study of the hyperactive child syndrome. *Biological Psychiat.* 3 (1971): 189-195.

Moss, H. A., and Kagan, J. Report on personality consistency and change from the Fels Longitudinal Study. *Vita Humana* 7 (1964): 127-139.

Moyer, K. E. *The Physiology of Hostility*. Chicago: Markham, 1971.

Muslin, H. L., and Pieper, W. J. On the ego restraint of violence. In *Dynamics of Violence*, edited by J. Fawcett. Chicago: A.M.A., 1971.

Mussen, P. H., Conger, J. J., and Kagan, J. J. *Child Development and Personality*, 2nd ed. New York: Harper & Row, 1963.

Naka, S., Abe, K., and Sizuki, H. Childhood behavior characteristics of the parents in certain behavior problems of children. *Acta Paedopsychiatrica* 32 (1965): 11-16.

Nelson, S. D. Nature/nurture revisited: a review of the biological bases of conflict. *J. of Conflict Resolution* 18 (1974): 285-335.

Offer, D. Coping with aggression among normal adolescent boys. In *Dynamics of Violence*, edited by J. Fawcett. Chicago: A.M.A., 1971.

O'Neal, P., and Robins, L. N. Childhood patterns predictive of adult schizophrenia. *Amer. J. Psychiat.* 115 (1958): 385-391.

O'Neill, D. Stress and disease: a review of principles. *Brit. Med. J.* 5091 (1958): 285-287.

Ostow, M. Parent's hostility to their children. *Israel Annals of Psychiat. & related Disc.* 8 (1971): 3-21.

Parens, H. Inner sustainment: Metapsychological considerations. *Psychoanal. Quart.* 39 (1970): 223-239.

_____ and Saul, L. J. *Dependence in Man*. New York: Internat. Univ. Press, 1971.

Parker, R. S., ed. *The Emotional Stress of War, Violence, and Peace*. Pittsburgh: Stanwix House, 1972.

Payne, R. *The Life and Death of Adolph Hitler*. New York: Praeger, 1973.

Pearson, G. H. J. The chronically aggressive child. *Psychoanal. Rev.* 26 (1939): 485-525.

Peck, R. F., and Havighurst, R. J. *The Psychology of Character Disorder*. New York: Wiley, 1960.

Pemberton, D. A., and Benady, D. R. Consciously rejected children. *Brit. J. Psychiat.* 123 (1973): 575-578.

Pokorny, A. D. Background factors in schizophrenia. *J. Nerv. and Ment. Dis.* 134 (1962): 84-87.

Prescott, E., and Jones, E. *The "Politics" of Day Care*. Washington, D.C.: National Association for the Education of Young Children, 1972.

Rado, S. *Psychoanalysis of Behavior*. New York: Grune & Stratton, 1956.

Rangell, L. Aggression, Oedipus, and historical perspective. *Internat. J. Psycho-Anal.* 52 (1972): 3-11.

Rank, B. Aggression. In *The Psychoanalytic Study of the Child*, 3: 43-48. New York: Internat. Univ. Press, 1949.

Rappaport, J. R. *The Clinical Evaluation of the Dangerousness of the Mentally Ill*. Springfield, Ill.: Charles C. Thomas, 1967.

Redl F., and Wineman, D. *Children Who Hate: The Disorganization and Breakdown of Behavior Concepts*. Glencoe, Ill.: Free Press, 1951.

Resnick, P. J. Child murder by parents: a psychiatric review of filicide. *Amer. J. Psychiat.* 126 (1969): 325-334.

Rheingold, H. L. To rear a child. *Amer. Psychologist* 28 (1973): 42-46.

Rice, E., Ekdahl, M., and Miller, L. *Children of Mentally Ill Parents*. New York: Behavioral Publ., 1971.

Richette, L. A. *Throwaway Children*. New York: Dell, 1970.

Ricks, D. F., and Berry, J. C. Family and symptom patterns that precede schizophrenia. In *Life History Research in Psychopathology*, vol. 1, edited by M. Roff and D. F. Ricks. Minneapolis: Univ. of Minnesota Press, 1970.

Robbins, P. R. Personality and psychosomatic illness: a selective review of research. *Genetic Psychol. Monogr.* 80 (1969): 51-90.

Robertson, J. Mothering as an influence on early development. In *The Psychoanalytic Study of the Child*, vol. 17. New York: Internat. Univ. Press, 1962.

Robins, L. N. *Deviant Children Grown Up: A Sociological and Psychiatric Study of Sociopathic Personality*. Baltimore: Williams & Wilkins, 1966.

Roche, P. Q. *Criminal Mind: A Study of Communication between Criminal Law and Psychiatry*. New York: Grove Press, 1959.

Roff, M., Mink, W., and Hinrichs, G. *Developmental Abnormal Psychology.* New York: Holt, Rinehart & Winston, 1966.

Roff, M., and Ricks, D. F., eds. *Life History Research in Psychopathology*, vol. 1. Minneapolis: Univ of Minnesota Press, 1970.

Roff, M., Robins, L. N., and Pollack, M., eds. *Life History Research in Psychopathology*, vol. 2. Minneapolis: Univ. of Minnesota Press, 1972.

Rosenthal, M. J., Finkelstein, M., Ni, E., and Robertson, R. E. A study of mother-child relationships in the emotional disorders of children. *Genet. Psychol. Monogr.* 60 (1959): 63-116.

Roth, M. Human violence as viewed from the psychiatric clinic. *Amer. J. Psychiat.* 128 (1972): 1043-1056.

Rothenberg, A. On anger. *Amer. J. Psychiat.* 128 (1971): 454-460.

Russell, D. H. A study of juvenile murderers. *J. of Offender Therapy* 3 (1965): 55-86.

Rutter, M. Psycho-social disorders in childhood and their outcome in adult life. *J. of Royal College of Physicians*, London 4 (1970): 211-218.

Salzman, L., and Masserman, J., eds. *Modern Concepts of Psychoanalysis.* New York: Philosophical Library, 1962.

Sanford, N. Dehumanization and collective destructiveness. *Internat. J. of Group Tensions* 1 (1971): 26-41.

Sargent, D. Children who kill: a family conspiracy. *Social Work* 7 (1962): 35-42.

Satten, J., Menninger, K., Rosen, I., and Mayman, M. Murder without apparent motive; a study in personality disorganization. *Amer. J. Psychiat.* 117 (1960): 48-53.

Saul, L. J. *The Bases of Human Behavior: A Biologic Approach to Psychiatry.* Westport, Conn.: Greenwood Press, 1971.

_____. Criminal acting out and psychopathology. In *Crime, Law and Corrections*, edited by R. Slovenko. Springfield, Ill.: Charles C. Thomas, 1965.

_____. *Emotional Maturity*, 3rd ed. Philadelphia: Lippincott, 1971.

_____. Hostility. In *Crime, Law, and Corrections*, edited by R. Slovenko. Springfield, Ill.: Charles C. Thomas, 1965.

_____. Inferiority feelings and hostility. *Amer. J. Psychiat.* 108 (1951): 120-122.

_____. Maternal love. In *The Meaning of Love*, edited by A. Montagu. New York, 1953.

_____. Physiological effects of emotional tension. In *Personality and Behavior Disorders*, vol. 1. New York: Ronald Press, 1944.

_____. *Psychodynamically Based Psychotherapy.* New York: Science House, 1972.

_____. Some psychological bases of war and peace. *Comp. Psychiat.* 2 (1961): 134-139.

Saul, L. J., and Lyons, J. W. Acute neurotic reactions. In *The Impact of Freudian Psychiatry*, edited by F. Alexander and H. Ross. Chicago: Univ. of Chicago Press, 1952.

Saul, L. J., and Sheppard, E. An approach to the ego functions. *Psychoanal. Quart.* 27 (1958): 237-246.

_____. An attempt to quantify emotional forces using manifest dreams. *J. Amer. Psychoanal. Assn.* 4 (1956): 486.

Saul, L. J., Sheppard, E., Selby, D., Lhamon, W., Sachs, D., and Master, R. The quantification of hostility in dreams with reference to essential hypertension. *Science* 110 (1954): 382.

Saul, L. J., and Wenar, S. Early influences on the development and disorders of personality. *Psychoanal. Quart.* 34 (1965): 327-389.

Scharr, J. H. Violence in juvenile gangs. *Amer. J. Orthopsychiat.* 33 (1963): 29-37.

Shoeck, H. Envy, *A Theory of Social Behavior*. New York: Harcourt, Brace and Jovanovich, 1966.

Schonecke, O. W., Schuffel, W., Schafer, N., and Winter, K. Assessment of hostility in patients with functional cardiac complaints. *Psychotherapy and Psychosomatics* 20 (1972): 272-281.

Schuffel, W., and Schonecke, O. W. Assessment of hostility in the course of psychosomatic treatment of three patients with functional disorders. *Psychotherapy and Psychosomatics* 20 (1972): 282-293.

Schur, M. *The Id and the Regulatory Principles of Mental Functioning*. J. Amer. Psychoanal. Assn. Monogr. Ser. No. 4 (1966).

Scott, J. P. *Aggression*. Chicago: Univ. of Chicago Press, 1958.

_____. Critical periods in behavior development. *Science* 138 (1962): 949-958.

Searles, H. F. The psychodynamics of vengefulness. *Psychiatry* 19 (1956): 31-39.

Sears, R. R., Maccoby, E. E., and Levine, J. *Patterns of Child Rearing*. New York: Harper & Row, 1957.

Selye, H. *The Physiology and Pathology of Exposure to Stress*. Montreal: Acta, 1950.

_____. Stress and psychiatry. *Amer. J. Psychiat.* 113 (1957): 423-427.

_____. *The Stress of Life*. New York: McGraw-Hill, 1956.

Sharma, S. L. Personality and crime. *Research J. of Philos. and Soc. Sci.* 2 (1965): 150-158.

Silver, H. K., and Kempe, C. H. Problem of parental criminal neglect and severe physical abuse of children. *J. Dis. Child* 95 (1959): 528.

Silver, L. B., Dublin, C. C., and Lourie, R. S. Does violence breed violence? Contributions from a study of the child abuse syndrome. *Amer. J. Psychiat.* 126 (1969): 404-407.

Solomon, G. F. Psychodynamic aspects of aggression, hostility, and violence. In *Violence and the Struggle for Existence*, edited by D. N. Daniels, M. F. Gilula, and F. M. Ochberg. Boston: Little, Brown, 1970.

Spiegel, J. P. Psychosocial factors in riots—old and new. *Amer. J. Psychiat.* 125 (1968): 281-285.

Spitz, R. A. Anaclitic depression: an inquiry into the genesis of psychiatric conditions in early childhood. In *The Psychoanalytic Study of the Child*, 1: 313-342. New York: Internat. Univ. Press, 1945.

_____. *The First Year of Life: A Psychoanalytic Study of Normal and Deviant Development of Object Relations*. New York: Internat. Univ. Press, 1965.

Stegenga, J. A. Personal aggressiveness and war. *Internat. J. of Group Tensions* 2 (1972): 22-36.

Steiner, L. R. *Understanding Juvenile Delinquency*. Philadelphia: Chilton, 1960.

Sterne, R. S. *Delinquent Conduct and Broken Homes: A Study of 1,050 Boys*. New Haven: College & Univ. Press, 1964.

Steward, L., and Livson, N. Smoking and rebelliousness: a longitudinal study from childhood to maturity. *J. of Consult. Psychol.* 30 (1966): 325-329.

Stone, L. Reflections on the psychoanalytic concept of aggression. *Psychoanal. Quart.* 40 (1971): 195-244.

Storr, A. *Human Aggression*. New York: Atheneum, 1968.

_____. *Human Destructiveness*. New York: Basic Books, 1972.

Suttie, I. D. *The Origins of Love and Hate*. New York: Julian Press, 1952.

Szasz, T. S. The role of hostility in the pathogenesis of peptic ulcer. *Psychosom. Med.* 60 (1947).

Textor, R. B. *A Cross-Cultural Summary*. New Haven: Human Resources Area Files Press, 1967.

Thorne, F. The etiology of sociopathic reactions. *Amer. J. Psychotherapy* 13 (1959): 319-330.

Tinbergen, N. On war and peace in animals and man. *Science* 160 (1968): 1411-1418.

_____. *Social Behavior in Animals*. New York: John Wiley, 1963.

Toch, H. H. *Violent Men: An Inquiry into the Psychology of Violence*. Chicago: Aldine, 1969.

Tolor, H., Warren, M., and Weinrich, H. M. Relation between parental interpersonal styles and their children's psychological distance. *Psychol. Rpts.* 29 (1971): 1263-1275.

Turnbull, C. M. *The Mountain People*. New York: Simon & Schuster, 1973.

Usdin, G., ed. *Perspectives on Violence*. New York: Brunner/Mazel, 1972.

Vogel, E. F. The marital relationship of parents of emotionally disturbed children: polarization and isolation. *Psychiatry* 23 (1960): 1-12.

Waring, M., and Ricks, D. F. Family patterns of children who became adult schizophrenics. *J. of Nerv. and Ment. Dis.* 140 (1965): 351-364.

Washburn, S. L., ed. Behavior in human evolution. In *Classification and Human Evolution*. (Viking Fund Publications in Anthropology, no. 37.) New York: Wenner-Gren Foundation for Anthropological Research, 1963.

_____. Conflict in primate society. In *Conflict in Society*, edited by A. De Reuck and J. Knight. Boston: Little, Brown, 1966.

_____. *Social Life and Early Man*. Chicago: Aldine, 1961.

Washburn, S. L., and Hamburg, D. A. Aggressive behavior in Old World monkeys and apes. In *Primates: Studies in Adaptation and Variability*, edited by P. C. Jay. New York: Holt, Rinehart and Winston, 1968.

Wasserman, L. H., ed. *Individual and Family Dynamics*. New York: Grune & Stratton, 1959.

Weissman, M., Fox, K., Klerman, G. L. Hostility and depression associated with suicide attempts. *Amer. J. Psychiat.* 130 (1973): 450-455.

Whithorn, J. C. Stress and emotional health. *Amer. J. Psychiat.* 112 (1956): 773-781.

Whiting, B. B. Sex identity conflict and physical violence: a comparative study. *Amer. Anthropology* 67 (1965): 123-140.

_____, ed. *Six Cultures: Studies in Child Rearing*. New York: John Wiley, 1963.

Whiting, J. W. M., Chasdi, E. H., Antonovsky, H. F., and Avril, B. C. The learning of values. In *People of Rimrock: A Study of Values in Five Cultures*, edited by E. Z. Vogt and E. M. Albert. Cambridge, Mass.: Harvard Univ. Press, 1966.

Wilkerson, D., and Cox, C. *Parents on Trial: Why Kids Go Wrong—or Right*. New York: Hawthorne Books, 1967.

Wilson, D. *My Six Convicts*. New York: Holt, Rinehart and Winston, 1951.

Winnick, H. Z., Moses, R., Ostow, M., eds. *Psychological Bases of War*. New York: Quadrangle Books, 1973.

Wolf, S. Life stress and patterns of disease. In *The Psychological Basis of Medical Practice*, edited by H. Lief, V. Lief, and N. Lief. New York: Hoeber Med. Div., Harper & Row, 1963.

Wolff, H. G. The mind-body relationships. In *An Outline of Man's Knowledge*. New York: Doubleday, 1960.

_____. *Stress and Disease*, 2nd ed. Revised and edited by D. Wolf and H. Goodell. Springfield, Ill.: Charles C. Thomas, 1968.

Wolfgang, M. E. Violence and human behavior. In *Psychology and the Problems of Society*, edited by F. F. Korten, S. W. Cook, and J. I. Lacey. Washington, D.C.: Amer. Psychological Assn., 1970.

_____, and Ferracuti, F. *The Subculture of Violence*. London: Tavistock: 1967.

Wolman, B. B. The empty bucket. *Internat. J. of Group Tensions* 1 (1971): 5-25.

_____. Human belligerence. *Internat. J. of Group Tensions* 2 (1972): 48-66.

Woods, R. L. *World of Dreams*. New York: Random House, 1947.

Zegans, L. S. Philosophical antecedents to modern theories of human aggressive instinct. *Psychoanal. Quart.* 42 (1973): 239-266.

Zilboorg, G. *The Psychology of the Criminal Act and Punishment* (Issac Ray Lectures, 1954). Westport, Conn.: Greenwood Press, 1968.

INDEX